McCORMICK'S REAPER

This reaper, first publicly demonstrated in July, 1831,
marked the beginning of the emancipation
of the American farmer

The American Cavalcade Series

FARMS
AND
FARMERS

THE STORY of AMERICAN AGRICULTURE

WILLIAM·H·CLARK
AUTHOR OF
"SHIPS AND SAILORS" AND "RAILROADS AND RIVERS"

ILLUSTRATED FROM PHOTOGRAPHS AND OLD PRINTS

L. C. PAGE & COMPANY (INC.)
Boston — Publishers

IN MEMORIAM

Dr. Wilbert G. A. Lindquist
My friend

FOREWORD

The story of the American farmer is an absorbing and fascinating chronicle composed both of human drama and economic development. To detail the history completely would be a task of enormous proportions. Indeed, the volumes resulting from such an effort would be so many that the whole would have little value for anyone not a specialist. Instead, it was desired to write a brief, straightforward account which would give as complete a picture as possible.

This entailed a great amount of labor in the selection of material. Actually, even in the final revision of the manuscript, at least a third of the thrice-sifted facts had to be eliminated. In consequence, much has had to be omitted that might well have been included.

However, it is hoped that the result has been a readable book which gives a clear and comprehensive picture of what has happened to the farms and the farmers of America during the past three hundred years. It furnishes, also, an indication of what these sturdy citizens, comprising a vital third of our nation, will face in the forthcoming troubled years that began with V-J Day.

ACKNOWLEDGMENT

So many persons have aided the writer of this history of farming in America that it would be difficult to mention them all. However, because of their considerable contributions, the author desires to express formal acknowledgment of gratitude to the following: Dr. Abbott Payson Usher, professor of economics, Harvard University; Everett E. Edwards, agricultural economist, Division of Statistics and Historical Research, United States Department of Agriculture; M. C. Merrill, chief of publications, Office of Information, United States Department of Agriculture; and Eve Grey of the Editorial Department of L. C. Page & Company.

WILLIAM H. CLARK

CONTENTS

xi

LIST OF ILLUSTRATIONS

INTRODUCTION

The dream of having a home and a bit of land is as old as civilization. In times of great upheavals it recurs with increased power. Today it is the dream many of our American soldiers have carried into battle, a hope that has supported them through years of bitter conflict. When these men return, some of them will realize their dream. Already there is a drive for the Government to provide farms for some of our fighting men.

Multitudes of warworkers, too, men and women who labored to bring about the miracle of American wartime industrial production, also want farms. These citizens, many of whom have more money than they ever have had before, were already buying land during the war. More farms were purchased in 1943 than in any other year on record,[1] and during 1944, farm purchases have continued to increase rapidly.

Claude R. Wickard, then Secretary of Agriculture, gave warning: ". . . the fever of rural land inflation has not only set in, but has reached a point of danger in many important agricultural areas."[2]

All this is understandable. There have been probably more than 12,000,000 men at one time in the armed services. They were uprooted from their homes, herded into camps, dressed in drab uniformity, and scattered to the furthest reaches of the world. They have lived under conditions of peril and of boredom which have reacted disastrously upon their ideas and emotions.

the back-to-the-farm march is lamentation. The authorities do warn against such a "dream-farm" as this:

". . . An attractive home in a rural setting, a devoted and helpful wife, happy and healthful children, good and friendly neighbors. There is a yard, a garden, an orchard, a barn and barn lot, and there are fields and pastures, streams, and wooded places. There are growing things you have planted and tilled with your own hands and later will harvest. There is livestock which you feed and care for. There is firsthand contact with things that are real and genuine; there are peace, quiet, communion with nature, security, independence, a chance to create your own destiny. This is a dream farm."[7]

In contrast, there is the "real farm":

"The real farm is no dream. Farming is a hard way of making a living. There is much physical labor about it . . . despite all modern machinery and labor-saving devices. Much farm work must be done in weather too hot, too cold, or too wet for comfort . . . Hazards are great. Frosts, floods, droughts, weeds, pests, and diseases of plants and animals often blast hopes of bountiful harvests and big profits . . . Cash returns are likely to be disappointingly small. The bright lights and the gay life of a city are not within easy reach, and they do not mix well with farming . . . Measured in dollars and cents, the odds are against your making anything more than modest returns."[8]

But the warnings conclude, generally, with a statement such as this: "If the conditions are met (capital, experience, and ability to labor intelligently), you should be able to live modestly but well on a farm. You may weather

hard times and depressions better than many people who depend upon employment in cities."⁹

Thus the American farmer finds himself face to face with a new age in agriculture, for the official warnings being issued to inexperienced, would-be farmers apply also to the men and women already practicing agriculture.

In the following chapters, which tell the story of American agriculture, two threads tie the happenings of the centuries together. One thread is our past careless exploitation of free land. That thread is now broken. There is no more free land. The second thread is the fact that in the past, farmers almost always, except in periods of financial depression, have enjoyed a good market. This nation has multiplied its population tremendously. Industry, since about 1825, constantly has withdrawn men and women from the soil into industry, and has also employed multitudes more. Each one of these workers has received wages and purchased farm products.

Thus, no matter how much overproduction the farmers wrenched from the soil, more often than not, in the past, the produce was all sold. Even the mechanization of agriculture, the emancipation of the farmer from brute labor, and the vast increase in his effective time and strength, failed to glut the market—until 1930. Before that, there was always a market. Now, the thread of an expanding market is also broken.

The farmer can no longer continue to follow the traditional American pattern. If he is to have his measure of prosperity in the great era just dawning, then he must make the most of every advantage he can grasp.

His greatest help will be *education*. Tomorrow, scien-

tific learning will be as vital to the farmer as practical experience has been in the past. The 4-H Clubs, the Grange,
the Agricultural Extension, the Farm Bureau—such farm
organizations have played an important role, but they are
just beginning to accept their responsibilities. Their influence tomorrow will be vast.

Even a generation back, scientific farming was an ideal
at which many a farmer jeered. Tomorrow, a BS in agriculture will be as important for a farmer as an MD to a
doctor. The uneducated farmer is already becoming a
part of past history.

Farming—modern farming—has become a profession,
and education is the first step required for success in its
practice. The quality of soil and soil products—rather
than widespread quantity—is the only hope for farming
of the future.

The story of how conditions today have developed from
the days when land was free and anyone could be a farmer
if he were willing to work, is vastly interesting and instruc-
tive. It is of importance to every American.

1, 2 *The Agricultural Situation.* Washington, D. C., June, 1944
3 Speech, August 23, 1944, at a hearing of the House Special Committee on Postwar Economic Policy and Planning.
4 *What Postwar Policies for Agriculture?* Washington, D. C. 1944
5, 6 *Land Policy Review.* U. S. Dept. of Agric. Vol. VII. No. 2. Summer, 1944
7, 8, 9 *Shall I Be A Farmer?* U. S. Dept. of Agri., Washington, D. C. 1944

PART I

SAVAGE AMERICA

CHAPTER I

ENGLAND—1600

EUROPE of the seventeenth century suffered widespread political and religious convulsions. The social order inherited from the Middle Ages was breaking up, with resulting chaos.

In England the spasms were widespread, though less violent than on the Continent. Even the rich were ruined by the economic drain of endless wars. Neither in the privacy of their homes nor in their work in the fields and shops were men secure. Each day brought the fear of being snatched and sold into the service of kings making war. Each day brought the fear of church officials and agents of the Crown coming to compel men and women to worship according to established forms.

More than all, because of overpopulation in England, poverty was becoming more and more universal and degrading. Even the middle class was held within narrow circumstances by the iron grip of tradition and lack of opportunity. Parents could see little hope of bettering their own condition, far less that of their children.

Into this way of life came news of America, of free land and boundless opportunity.

"Land, land! Our own farms!"

The news gave hopeless men and women a dream of

3

liberty, of security—a chance to better themselves. The most daring and the most hard-pressed left England first, and others followed. Paupers who lacked the price of a passage westward could bind themselves to serve as laborers for from five to seven years. When their servitude was ended, they, too, could have land.

Ambition and Aspiration

Despite burdens of poverty, religious slavery, and social serfdom, at first only a few brave souls actually uprooted themselves and risked the hazard for freedom. About those Englishmen who first sailed westward there was a distinct quality that still sings over the century. Once aroused, they found in themselves an overflowing measure of energy and enterprise.

They were driven by ambition and aspiration which could not be damned by tradition. The qualities thus demonstrated in these first Americans—and similar characteristics in those who migrated from England and other countries in the years that followed—have given to this nation something of its uniquely powerful nature.

Because of this quality of determination and daring, the colonization of America began. Favorites of the King, backed by wealthy, adventurous merchants, had taken over vast tracts of English America and organized themselves into Companies, such as the London Company and the Plymouth Company. Their holdings were really of no value unless colonists could be persuaded to settle in the wilderness. Hence the Companies employed acts of propaganda to stimulate immigration.

In fact, extravagant advertising was necessary. The vast areas of emptiness overseas had to be peopled. Only

THE BEGINNINGS OF A FARM IN THE WILDERNESS

by building up many new settlements could white owners push the "bloody savages" out of this property. Only by building up towns and harbors could military forces be based in sufficient strength to win for England the conflict with the Spanish, the Dutch, and the French for this new wilderness of land.

The propagandists had plenty of material to work with. The explorers Drake and Hawkins had very pleasantly demonstrated by English piracies the vast wealth that Spain was milking out of its part of the New World. English ships lay in wait in the West Indies to snatch Spanish ships headed homeward from South America loaded with gold and silver stolen from the Incas Indians of Peru and elsewhere.

Even after the Spaniards had stopped dreaming of picking up a pocketful of jewels and of shoveling gold into the hold of a ship, legends of fabulous Indian cities of gold still persisted.

Then there was the fur trade. It was less romantic but certainly profitable. For a few trinkets the Indians were willing to turn over priceless pelts of beaver, fox, and mink, or to move back into the forest and give the first newcomers room.

Of course, fur trading was a risky business. Many a brave man set out and never returned. Still, the rewards were great.

It was a time when rough piracy on the high seas was an attractive profession, even for gentlemen, and no ordinary citizen thought himself unusual if he employed unscrupulous means in securing good business. In trading for furs, he was ready to risk some unpleasantness at the hands of the savages.

Tales About America

There was plenty of true information obtainable about real conditions. Fishermen had resorted to the New England coast for a hundred years before the first Pilgrims arrived. Many a gentleman explorer found some of these hardy fishers already crudely established in the better harbors. These fishermen, tough sea dogs from England and France, often replenished the food stores of the explorers, helped them repair their ships, and pointed the way up and down the uncharted coast.

The fishermen, upon returning home to England, had plenty to say of the bitter cold of the American winter, the heat of its summer, and the dark and forbidding aspect of its forests—not to mention the strange ways of the American Indians.

For the most part, the fishermen's accounts were word-of-mouth stories; but many a younger son of the nobility and many a lad destined for the church or the army also adventured overseas. Such educated men wrote home. Then there were the published accounts of famed adventurers like Raleigh, John Smith, and others.

Some of the tales about America were weird. For example, a copper plate reproduced by Hedrick[1] from a volume by Arnoldus Montanus and published in Amsterdam in 1671 shows a forest scene in America. A ferocious griffin is tearing out the throat of a curious-looking unicorn, while an animal something like a moose is stabbing his antlers into a wild horse. Still another animal, a cross between a wild boar and a lion, is battling with another hybrid, this one a cross between a tiger and a beaver. There are no maples and pines in the forest; there are only very tall palms.

Although such extreme descriptions were uncommon, most writers did give play to their imaginations in describing the wealth of animals which yielded furs, the multitudes of fish, and the fertility of the soil.

The writers usually neglected to describe the hosts of insects, the mosquitoes, gnats, chiggers, and ants that abounded in the wild new country. Nor did they trouble to mention such a frightening thing as malaria, which racked the adventurers with "the shakes," "the ague," or just plain "chills and fever." Nor did the accounts speak of the vast loneliness of the empty continent and the dire hardships of beginning life anew in such an unknown wilderness.

England Was No Eden

It is quite probable that we somewhat overemphasize these hardships today. In fact, the first English settlers in America, even those of the middle class, had not been commonly accustomed to a superabundance of comfort. England in 1620, for example, was largely rural. William Bradford,[2] declared:

"(We) . . . were used to a plaine countrie life and the innocente trade of husbandrey."

Rural England then was far from being developed. Only about twenty-five per cent of the country was under cultivation. The rest included forests, parks, moors, fens, and the great hunting parks of the gentry, which were never allowed to be touched by cultivation. There were few fences in the England of that day. Fields were separated by banks of earth overgrown with hedges. There were not many good roads. Most of the public ways were

rough tracks over which only broad-tired carts could move easily.

Social life was polished enough for the comparatively small group of the wealthy, but the vast majority of English folk lived close to empty stomachs and labored, when they could find employment, from sunup to sundown for a very poor living indeed. The food was rough and coarse and certainly little better than was available in the American wilderness. Meat, in particular, so plentiful in America, was scarce and costly. The common diet featured cabbages, turnips, and bread.

[1] Hedrick, Ulysses P. *History of Agriculture in New York.* 1933
[2] Bradford, Wm. *History of Plymouth Plantation.* Boston. 1898

CHAPTER II

THE FOREST

THE stories about America that were transmitted throughout England could not adequately have described the one mighty feature of America—the forest.

Picture a man and his wife as they stood in the gray light of some dawn and caught their first glimpse of the new country that was to be their home. Behind them were months of weary voyaging—reeling decks; salt crusted on everything, even their clothes and their faces; wretched food and putrid water.

Their ship had at last anchored offshore. At the first glimmer in the east they had clambered up on deck, and there before them lay America. Ashore could be seen a scattered group of rough houses—unpainted, windowless, and with roofs of sod or logs and chimneys of sticks daubed with mud. From the houses stretched rough fields dotted with charred stumps of trees. Beyond that, as far as the eye could see up and down the coast, lay the forest.

The wife clutched the arm of her husband. "I never dreamed 'twould be as wild looking as this," she whispered fearfully.

"Never mind, girl; we're here, and we'll make the best of it," replied her man. "Always remember, no matter what comes, we'll be free! And we'll have a bit of land to call our own."

But he, too, looked long at the great forest crowding the
settlement, uncharted, unknown, menacing.

So Dense a Forest

It was a magnificent growth, this forest. It covered,
roughly, the entire eastern half of the continent, although
the new settlers had no knowledge of that at the time.
Here and there were natural openings carpeted with wiry
grass or flat areas of swamps and winding meadows paral-
leling the rivers. In the main, however, the aspect was of
tangled woodland, felted hill, and valleys. Only in the
mountains did bare hilltops show their weathered granite.

This forest was filled with animals and wild Indians
that imagination had magnified into fierce horrors. A
man made his way through it with great toil and trouble,
unless he followed an animal or Indian trail or waded up
a stream. He had to wedge his way among tree trunks and
scramble over fallen timber. He was always on the alert
for a bear, a wolf, a wildcat, or the shadow of a skulking
Indian. He was ever becoming lost in the confusion. One
book[1] tells of explorers making their way north through
New Hampshire by sighting ahead from one hilltop to
the next, like mariners in a fog grouping along from one
buoy to the next.

The Northern Forest

In the main, the English colonists faced what modern
forestry authorities call the Northern Forest Region.[2]
This covered (and still does, in part) most of New England, New York, and adjacent Canada and extended
southward to Georgia in the Allegheny plateau and westward into the Lake States. This was one of the world's
greatest forest treasuries.

HEAVY FORESTS COVERED MUCH OF AMERICA

By 1890 it had been almost completely ravaged. Save for a few isolated stands and for the National Parks and Forests, it is today for the most part but a miserable second and third growth, a mere echo of its former majestic extent.

The Indian deeply revered the great forest as an abundant source of life. He felt very close to the Great Power that had given it to him. Small wonder, then, that he viewed in terror the white man's wanton destruction of that vast storehouse.

Evergreens and Hardwoods

The colonist facing this forest found the white pine his chief source of construction material. This wonderful tree was the most valuable of all American species. Out of its firm white substance the colonist built his home and made his kitchen utensils. From white pine he reared his church, his school, and his town hall. From it he built his ships, when foreign trade developed. For the first two hundred and fifty years of its existence, all America was built up from the wood of the white pine.

There were other evergreens in the Northern Forest. There was the hemlock, which gave bark for tanning the colonist's leather and feathery boughs to make his bed. There was the spruce, long considered to be a mere obstruction to be removed from land to be tilled, until it was discovered recently to be the best raw material for paper. And there was the fir, another tough tree which had to be removed and burned up before crops could be grown. Today it is valuable for timber and pulp, since American white pine and spruce are nearly exterminated.

And there were the hardwoods. From the maples, the

Indians taught the settlers to make sugar. There was bass-wood—soft white wood for the settler's bowls and plates. The oaks were considered a nuisance, at first, because their fibers were so tough to work; but later they were priceless as framing for houses, wood for furniture, and timbers for ships. These are only the few most important trees. Actually there were more than eight hundred species of forest trees in this great Northern Region.[3]

The Central Hardwoods

Settlers in the rest of America, outside of the Northern Forest, were much less fortunate in their timber. Those colonists who later ventured westward and crossed through the Northern Forest into the valleys of the Ohio and Mississippi, and those who scattered into the foothills of the Appalachians, settled in what is now called the Central Hardwood Forest. This forest lacked the valuable white pine, in particular. It contained oaks, elms, poplars, and ashes—but these were of use to the settler only for building his log cabin and for fencing his fields.

The Southern Forest

From New Jersey, south along the coast into Texas and the western and southern section of the Mississippi Valley, the English, Spanish, and French settlers found themselves in a more open forest. It was marked by the towering, straight stems of the hard pines—the yellow and the longleaf. At first these species were considered useless; but in time the farmers found them to be a gold mine. From their trunks were made masts for ships; from their resins were distilled turpentine and tar.

Other trees in this Southern Forest were the gums, the

cottonwood, and the cypress. The Spanish at St. Augustine and the French at New Orleans found and used the live oak, the palmetto, the hard pine, and the cypress. The levels of Florida and the bayous of Louisiana were rich in these species. They were of not the slightest commercial value, however, to the early Southerners, who ignored them and used stone for building purposes.

Westward beyond the Mississippi the forests were replaced by great rolling grasslands which were more and more arid toward the mountains. There were a few trees, mostly along the watercourses; but these aspens, cottonwoods, and oaks were generally worthless, save for local building and fuel.

The Mountain Forests

The newcomers, spreading their settlements on into the sunset, in due time arrived in the fourth type of forest, the Rocky Mountain Forest Region. This forest is much unlike the Northern Forest. Instead of growing in a thick stand and almost continuous over a great area, it is more like a patchwork quilt of groups of trees interspersed with barren rock. Water is not abundant in this area, and trees grow only where they find it.

The important trees in this Mountain Region were the ponderosa pine, the lodge-pole pine, the Douglas fir, and the Engleman spruce. There was hemlock in the North; cottonwood and cedar flourished in the Mid-section; as did oak, sycamore, and aspen in the South. For the settlers, these were sufficient for homes, fences, and fuel.

Pacific Coast Forests

The Spaniards plunged through the desert into California. The French, English, and American fur traders,

each in their time, followed the fur trade into the Oregon
Territory. These exploring settlers found still different
types of forest. Pastoral Spanish California was an Arca-
dia which endured until the gold rush of 1849. There were
huge trees which amazed the pioneers, such as the red-
wood, the sequoia, and the sugar pine. Wherever they
have been spared, these sturdy, beautiful giants still thrill
the traveler.

The Northwest, that territory which now comprises
Washington and Oregon, was one of the world's grandest
forest lands. The magnificent Sitka spruce, hemlock,
Douglas fir, and Western cedar towered into the sky in
such breath-taking height that they defied the axe for
many years. Not until modern power saws were invented
was their serious exploitation made possible.

Forest Ruin

These great American forests were a priceless heritage,
our most marvelous natural resource. Their destruction
must be counted as one of the most shocking examples of
reckless consumption of valuable assets that our nation
has perpetrated.

Of course, in the beginning, some cutting away of the
forest was necessary. The farmer, taking up new land, had
to clear it before he could plant his seeds. But the axe
alone could never have dropped the trees quickly enough.
The farmer therefore chipped off a girdle in the bark of
each giant tree. As soon as the trees were dead, the torch
was applied—and thus, in time, the beautiful American
forest vanished in smoke. Probably, long before 1700, the
settlers destroyed more wood than even such a prodigal
nation as ours has consumed since then.

A Wooden Civilization

America was and still is a wood-using nation. The Europeans came from a land where wood was expensive and jealously guarded. Stone and brick were building materials, particularly in England.

Once in America, the farmer found trees so abundant that he created a civilization out of wood. He built his house and his public buildings of wood. He made tools of wood, set the table with wooden dishes, built bridges of wood, and even paved the roads in swampy regions with wood. The traditional Yankee backwoodsman whittled out from the forest innumerable things needed on the farm. Wooden pegs were even used in place of nails. And this traditional Yankee backwoodsman was the pattern of all American colonists.

The great conquest of the forest was the first page of the national epic. By conquering the forest America was able to exist in its westward-moving frontier. From direct use of some of the wood, and its use as a by-product of the clearing of the land, came a great wealth of products—while the wood lasted. The farmer sold logs, timber, fuel, charcoal, pearl ash (potash for soap), tanning bark, wood ashes as a fertilizer for acid soil, sugar, and ships' masts. From the abundant wild life came meat, fats, feathers, and furs. Actually, the axe and the rifle produced more wealth in America for many years than did the plow and the hoe.

Wild Food

No present-day hunter can picture the abundance of wild life in early America—the fish in the rivers and along the seashores, the wild animals, and the birds. There

were times when the sky was literally darkened by birds.
James Fenimore Cooper in *Chainbearer* describes one
species of bird, the lovely passenger pigeon:

"As we drew near to the summit of the hill, pigeons
began to be seen fluttering among the branches over our
heads . . . We had probably seen a thousand birds glanc-
ing around among the trees before we came in view of the
roost itself. The numbers increased as we drew nearer,
and presently the forest was alive with them.

"The fluttering was incessant and often startling as we
passed ahead, our march producing a movement in the
living crowd that really became confounding. Every tree
was literally covered with nests . . . The place had the
odor of a fowl-house, and squabs just fledged sufficiently
to trust themselves in short flights, were fluttering around
us in all directions, in tens of thousands. . . . The masses
moved before us precisely as a crowd of human beings
yields to a pressure of danger on any given point; the
vacuum created by its passage filling in its rear as the
waters of the ocean flow into the track of a keel . . ."

And of such multitudes, not one passenger pigeon is
left today. All have been slaughtered!

An impressive picture could be drawn of the bison, the
shaggy buffalo that supported the Plains Indians only to
vanish before the tide of greedy white settlement. Some
herds of bison had worked through the mountain passes of
the East, but they roamed the middle sections and the
Western Plains by the thousands.

The Indians hunted them for food, carefully selecting
for the kill only a number sufficient for their needs. The
white man, however, killed not only for meat but for
sport. Hunting parties traveled far and wide to kill buf-

falo merely for the excitement of it and left the carcasses to rot upon the plains.

Similarly, there was at first a great abundance of game, such as deer, grouse, ducks, and geese; and also cod, trout, and bass. Some of these remain today. But the caribou and the beaver are vanished from the woods, and the valuable salmon and sturgeon no longer can be found in our waters.

Fertile Soil

Small wonder remains that Englishmen finally left their homes by the thousands. They exchanged European poverty, misery, and the straight-jacket of tradition for the wealth, happiness, freedom, and limitless opportunity of the great forest overseas. Once the three thousand miles of ocean crossing had been endured, any man with a strong back and a fund of patience could establish himself, a peer of his fellows.

In one respect at least the propaganda of the London Company and the Plymouth Company in England in recruiting settlers did not exaggerate. The farmer really found the soil fertile. The reason was that it had been enriched for untold centuries by the natural cycle of plant life. It was a reservoir rich in the humus accumulated through unmeasured time. Any seed planted in it, given sun and air, would grow. Even the burning away of the forest provided salts which enriched the land still further.

Of the complexity and diversity of American soils, the first American farmer knew very little. Of the results of overcropping, the impoverishment that annual planting causes, he knew still less. Of the lowering of the water table by the destruction of the forest cover and of the erosion of the topsoil from bared land, he was quite unaware.

Such knowledge was to come more than two centuries later, when in many sections of our country it was almost too late.

The America the settler found was an agricultural paradise. There were no insect pests that destroyed crops; nor had he to fight any of the bacterial and fungus diseases so pestilential today. These were not the only blessings. The beauty of America in the early days played its role. The grace of leafy hills and plains must have fascinated the newcomers, as did the boundless open life that was free of domineering aristocracy and tradition.

But it was a wild and untamed beauty. The colonists were forced to reduce life to its lowest terms as they landed and then marched westward to the Pacific. There was red murder behind many a tree, and there was cold and misery at every shoulder. But there was land for everyone; and America became a community of farmers, the first step in creating the nation-to-be.

There was abundant wealth yet untapped—coal, oil, gold, silver, and copper. Even the granite of the stubborn hills was prospective wealth. But in the beginning, it was the soil of the continent that was important—the vast reaches of unsettled country, of land that was the property of the first man to step upon it and to make it his home.

[1] *History of Washington, N. H.* No author. Published by the town. 1870
[2, 3] Perry, Josephine and Slauson, Celeste. *Forestry and Lumbering.* New York. 1939

CHAPTER III

THE INDIANS' BEQUEST TO THE COLONISTS

THE American colonists, of whom at least ninety per cent in the English settlements were farmers, had difficulties in adjusting themselves to the wilderness. But, wild as the country was, it was supporting the Indians, and from the Indians the farmer and his wife learned a new way of living.

There was usually plenty to eat—fish, game, fruit, berries, and the great Indian trio of corn, beans, and pumpkins. The white farmer had to learn from the Indian brave how to fish and to hunt, and how to grow the strange new crops. The farmer's wife had to learn from the Indian squaw how to gather the fruits and berries of the woods, and how to use these new foods. The farmer and his wife were face to face with the problem of basic survival. The Indian was their teacher, who demonstrated how a family could live on primitive terms.

These Indians were of widely varied character. In the southern Spanish regions the native tribes were comparatively highly civilized and, at least in Mexico and Peru, were very wealthy. They provided the Spanish conquistadores with the most marvelous loot of Christian times in gold, silver, and jewels.

Along the Atlantic shore, from the Saint Lawrence river to Florida, the tribes were for the most part

wretched primitives; but even so, there were degrees of culture among them. Some were merely clans of marauding nomads. Other tribes were more or less settled upon hunting grounds which they defended fiercely and ably from their neighbors. Still others, like those in what is now New York and its neighboring areas, were organized into the famous Five Nations.

In some of the English settlements, at least at first, relations between the settlers and the Indians were reasonably genial and honorable. Roger Williams and William Penn are outstanding examples of leadership in peaceful relations. As a result, the farmers learned quickly what the Indians had to teach. More than one settlement was saved from starvation by corn and game which the Indians provided in times of famine.

Unfortunately, concord between settlers and Indians proved to be exceptional and nowhere long endured. It could not last, for the farmers had to occupy the space the Indians considered their own. Human nature also soon exhibited its cruelty and stupidity. Individuals among the white newcomers, some of whom were interested in fur trading, and some of whom wanted new land and always more new land, soon began to cheat, to betray, and even to kill their Indian neighbors.

The Indians, by nature sensitive and bellicose, struck back. That their weapons were the silent arrow and the vicious tomahawk, that their methods were ambuscade, fire, and torture, only aggravated the conflict. The new settlers quickly added Indian fighting methods to their own. Mutual hatred, once begun, flamed high and demanded the extinction, root and stock, of one side or the other in the struggle.

As the years passed, and the Indians were either slain or pushed farther westward, the wars became ever more bloody and desperate. Only eternal vigilance, forts, punitive expeditions for killing off Indians, and actual battles made it possible for the farmer and his wife to exist along the frontier as it moved westward.

The Indian Teacher

Despite this terror, American agriculture had its roots in what the white farmer and his wife learned from the Indian brave and squaw. Essentially, this bequest from the Indian divides itself into two parts: methods of cultivation and the acquisition of new plants. The importance of each was tremendous.

First, the Indian method of planting corn, potatoes, beans, and other native New World crops remains the fundamental system of planting these crops. It is today the "hill system" of cultivation, as opposed to the Old World method of broadcast-sowing, as of grains.[1] Secondly, the economic plants domesticated by the Indian and given to the white farmer even now constitute about four sevenths of the value of all farm produce.[2]

Berries, Fish, and Game

The white farmer, accustomed in England to growing grain and such things as turnips and cabbages, would certainly have starved to death swiftly had it not been for the Indian's crops and his methods of growing them.

Of course, there were plenty of wild fruits, berries, fish, and game seasonally available. These wild foods varied in kind and quantity rather sharply with the latitude. Blueberries, blackberries, raspberries, gooseberries, cranber-

ries, and strawberries were to be found in considerable quantity. So were such wild fruits as cherries, grapes, and crabapples, and also various nuts.

Recording botanists were not common among the farmers, and it is not known today exactly just what wild foods were used; but one authority[3] on the subject, considering only the wild materials still in use today, lists sixty-nine species of edible fruits and berries, twenty-six species of salad plants and potherbs, fifteen species of nuts, thirteen species used as beverages and flavorings, and ten species of seed and pod-bearing plants. He lists a very large number of additional species which have been used as food in the past and are today still in use locally.

In addition, there were foods taken from the waters and the tidal flats: fish, clams, oysters, and lobsters. Game also was of marvelous abundance: deer, bear, moose, caribou, partridges, ducks, geese, swans, turkeys, pigeons, and many other varieties.

The trouble with this lavish quantity of food was that, for the most part, it was seasonable. It was not a year-round supply. The farmer could hunt and fish, but game was not always to be found. Indians themselves were frequently on the verge of starvation in the winter. The farmer's wife and children could pick berries, when they were ripe. But this meant either a feast or a famine, for the farmer had no way of preserving them, save drying, for the long months when the woods were bare.

Work or Starve

For the American farm family, it was a case of work or starve. It is because of this situation that the colonial farmer and his family believed so fervently in work as a

Yale University Press

INDIAN CORN CULTURE
Squanto teaching the Pilgrims how to grow corn
From a painting by C. W. Jefferys

virtue. Thus, although wild game, fish, fruits, and berries did help to feed the farm family, it was upon carefully cultivated and harvested crops that their daily existence really depended.

In the next chapter the European inheritance of the settler is described. Here it is the Indian bequest that is being considered.

There is a well-known tradition that the Indian lived a glorious life of ease; that he spent his time hunting and fishing in a sort of perpetual vacation. His squaw scratched the earth with a pointed stick, dropped in a few seeds, and in due time gathered a bountiful harvest. The early white farmer and his wife knew otherwise. They had to adopt the Indian system of agriculture—and it proved as laborious as it was successful.

The improvement of Indian methods of cultivation was the white farmer's contribution to agriculture. The Indians did not have draft animals. They used their own muscles. All the toil of planting, cultivating, and harvesting was done by hand. Nor did the Indians have tools, in the modern sense. The tools employed for cultivation were usually of wood—sharp-pointed implements for making furrows and spade-like blades for opening the soil, together with a hoe-like implement, often nothing more than a clamshell lashed to a stick.

For harvesting, the Indians simply broke away the heads of corn and scraped the kernels free with knives of stone or shell. It was the early colonist who in time brought in the horse and the ox from Europe to save his own back. And he it was who subsequently developed our modern elaborate machines in order to save time and to multiply effort.

Corn

Of all Indian food crops, corn was the most important, both to the Indian and to the white farmer. Easy to grow on new land, free from disease, it gave a bountiful return and was ideal for storage. Ears of corn needed only a dry place and protection against rodents to keep unchanged from one harvest to the next.

Corn came first to the farmer's table as the "roasting ear" along in early August. Compared with our sweet corn of today, these Indian varieties, probably similar to white flint and white dent, would seem very floury and rather tasteless. But in those early days the coming of the green corn was a time of rejoicing. The Indians celebrated it with a special corn feast. The unhusked ears were covered over with hot ashes or else were husked and then held over a bed of coals on the end of a pointed stick, the other end of which was set diagonally in the ground.

More like a modern dish was the Indian's succotash, a mixture of green corn kernels and shell beans boiled together. Sometimes the Indians added pumpkin and chopped meat, usually venison. The farmers adopted this dish with enthusiasm, and it was a hearty staple of late summer meals.

The farmers learned to char corn along in September, as the Indians did. The ears, still milky but with the starch well set, were roasted for hours over beds of coals until they were thoroughly dried and the kernels could be scraped off. This was actually the Indian method of dehydration. The blackened, flint-like kernels were not particularly palatable, but they kept indefinitely without spoiling. Later, when boiled in water, they made a nourishing meal. When traveling through the woods, the set-

tler carried a small bag of this dried corn to supplement whatever meat he could kill on the way.

The Indians also taught the white farmer to mix this charred corn with chopped venison and hard fat for hunting rations. This American version of sausage was the "K-ration" of the time. A roll of it sealed in a skin case was enough food to sustain a hunter or fur trader for many days, even if he did not find game.

Along in late September or in October, the corn was ripe, its kernels hard as rock. It was the great staple food of the colonial farm family. The ears were simply husked and then heaped in vermin-proof cribs until needed. Sometimes the corn was hulled by soaking in a lye made of water and wood ashes. The removal of the hard outer coating of the kernel made it possible to eat the whole seeds when boiled. Hulled corn is still an occasional article of diet in some parts of rural New England.

The first farmers seldom made use of hulled corn; they did not have the time in which to prepare it. Most often the dry, flint-like corn was shelled from the ears and the kernels pounded to a meal in the family kitchen. Usually the housewife used a stone pestle to hammer the kernels in a heavy wooden bowl. The farmer called the coarse meal which resulted "hominy," or sometimes "samp." It was much rougher in texture than the corn meal which is used today.

In every farm home this samp was a staple article of diet that was almost always warming in an iron kettle hanging from a crane in the kitchen fireplace. Usually the dish was simply the ground corn plus water and salt. If available, fat and even meat from wild game, usually deer, were added.

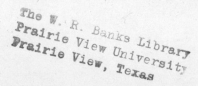

This was the method of actually cooking the corn that the farm wife learned from the Indian squaw. She also concocted several other ways of using it, however. One of the favorites was Indian pudding—a mixture of corn meal and water sweetened with maple sugar (another wild food the Indians showed the whites how to make). In time, when the great American triangular trade of rum, slaves, and molasses with the West Indies sprang up, this Indian pudding was sweetened with molasses, to its great enrichment.

Then there was a corn bread that the farm wives evolved. It was simply a hard, unleavened corncake made by kneading corn meal, water, and fat of some sort into a dough and baking it on flat stones before a fire. Of course, the farm wife eventually made better forms of corn bread, sometimes by the addition of yeast and maple sugar. Variously called johnnycake in the North and corn pone in the South, this corn bread is still a staple farm food, nourishing and delicious.

Beans

The beans grown by the Indians were of the shell type, as they are known today. The method of culture was intertwined with the growing of corn. With the Indians showing him how, the white farmer first burned the ground as clear as possible. Then, going around the "staghorns" of charred stumps that remained standing until they rotted away, he dug out shallow holes, spacing them about four feet apart on centers.

In each hole a fish, if available, was buried as fertilizer and covered over with soil. Into the shallow hole thus left, a half dozen grains of corn were thrown, together with a

few beans and a few pumpkin seeds. Then the hole was filled up and trod upon to "firm down" the soil.

As the corn grew, earth was drawn up around the stems by means of a hoe, thus creating the method of "hilling" which is still so widely practiced. The corn grew more rapidly than the beans and thus provided support for the vines when they appeared. The pumpkins simply sprawled wherever they could.

If you drive through New England today and see a thrifty field of corn supporting bean vines, with the great leaves of pumpkin and squash carpeting the ground below, you are not looking at a system of agriculture the Yankee has developed. You see an exact reproduction of the Indian cornfield which the first Puritans and Pilgrims copied. It is one that has never changed. It suits the soil and the climate.

Besides the hilling of the corn, the only other labor cultivation was weeding and keeping birds and animals away. These jobs were usually the work of young children.

The Indians, of course, knew nothing about soil exhaustion and the rotation of crops. They did learn that their corn and beans grew better if they were planted in new land every few years. Accordingly, the white farmer, who had plenty of land at first, commonly followed this practice. Later on the settlements became so crowded that succeeding farmers were forced to use the same land over and over again.

The extent of Indian agriculture and the richness of the soil can be visualized in the fact that, sketchy and laborious as corn growing was, the Indians must have produced at least a million bushels a year.[4]

The exact species of bean the Indians grew is not

known. Possibly it was some type of the red kidney bean, *Phaseolus vulgaris*. Commonly, the Indians used them in the early fall as shell beans, boiled in water, or boiled with corn, as succotash. The beans that remained were beaten out of the mature vines with sticks and then stored for winter. Probably they were boiled; for the Indians did not (in the forest regions, at least) have pottery strong enough for baking beans. The baked bean of New England, rich with molasses and drenched with salt pork fat, is evidently an improvement invented by the white farm wife.

The bean was an important food for the Indian. It was stored away safely in baskets woven from grasses, reeds, and wooden splints. In the winter, when game and fish were scarce, these beans were the chief source of protein. In exactly the same way the bean served the white farmer.

Pumpkins

The place of the pumpkin was not important, although the farmer adopted it eagerly and welcomed it as a vegetable that could be preserved for some months into the winter. The species the farmer found the Indians growing cannot now be identified with any degree of assurance. What we call the pumpkin was grown; we know that. A sort of warty summer squash was also commonly produced. But there does not seem to have been any winter squash such as, for example, our Blue Hubbard. Of the Indians' squashes, Josselyn[5] wrote:

". . . The squashes . . . a kind of melon or rather gourd, for they often degenerate into gourds. Some of them are green, some yellow, some longish like a gourd, others round like an apple, all of them pleasant food boiled and buttered and seasoned with spice . . ."

Incidentally, gourds were grown by the Indians and quickly planted by the new American farmers, but not as a food crop. They were used for utensils in the barn and kitchen. Their hard shells made them serve very well in the place of tinware and china.

Other Indian Crops

The potato, today so important as a food, was not much esteemed at first by English white farmers in the South, although the Spanish in their territories did make use of it quickly enough. In time, of course, the potato was generally adopted, particularly after it had been taken over to Europe and then returned to America in somewhat improved varieties.

Such was also the history of the South American tomato. The sweet potato and the yam, staples in the South, were similarly slighted by the English, but French and Spanish settlers quickly learned the value of these two roots and made adequate use of them.

Two plants the Indians grew were never adopted by white farmers to any degree, and they have long since been ignored. One is the wild onion, probably *Allium tricoccum*. Of course the settlers could harvest these wild; but they never cultivated them, for the European onion was far superior. The other Indian plant is the Jerusalem artichoke, a wild sunflower. We grow it now as a garden flower, forgetting that it was a highly important source of food for the Southern and Western Indians. The tuber is both palatable and nutritious. Perhaps some Burbank will go to work on it and some day give modern agriculture another interesting crop.

As for fruits and berries, the white farmer, amply sup-

plied with the wild species and devoted to the fruits
brought over from Europe, never bothered with the one
fruit the Indians did cultivate. This was the Canada
Plum, *Prunus nigra.* It seems to have been cultivated in
Canada, by the Five Nations in New York, and probably
elsewhere. The Indians did not eat the ripe fruits while
they were fresh, but dried them as prunes, storing them in
baskets for winter use. Of these plum-prunes, Cartier
wrote in 1534,[6] ". . . the Indians make prunes by soaking
the plums in lye and then drying them in the sun . . ."

Tobacco

Finally, there was the greatest bequest from the Indian
to the white man—tobacco. It is not a food, but it certainly
is a major crop. It is emphatically an American plant.
The Frenchman, Jean Nicot[7], managed to have his name
used as the botanical name, *Nicotiana,* but that is the only
thing European about tobacco.

Along the southern region of the Atlantic seaboard the
Indians found tobacco growing wild, like a weed. Elsewhere, climate permitting, they cultivated a long-leaved
variety. The Indians never improved their wild strains.
They also failed to enjoy the herb to the limit of its pos-
sibilities, because they did not cure it properly. They
grew the wild species of their region, and when the plants
were mature, hung them up to dry in the sun. They stored
the dry tobacco in a logan, or tepee. The Indian simply
pulled off a few leaves from the stem and crumpled them
into a pouch when he wanted a supply to smoke.

It was the white farmer who improved the plant by selection and then developed proper methods of curing, so
that the leaves could be packed and exported to England.

INDIAN AGRICULTURE
Indian village with maize and squash fields
From De Bry's Travels, 1556

And it was the white man who invented the cigar, the cigarette, and snuff. The Indian simply used a pipe, a cumbersome affair of red sandstone or talc, with a long reed or hollow branch for a stem.

Nevertheless the Indian did enjoy tobacco, and his white neighbor was not slow to follow suit. Cartier[8] has this to say of the Indians' use of it:

"There groweth also a certain kind of herbe, whereof in Summer they (the Indians) make greate provision for all the yeare, making a good account of it, and only men use it, and first they cause it to be dried in the Sunne, then weare it about their neckes wrapped in a little beaste's skin made like a little bagge, with a hollow peece of stone or wood like a pipe: then when they please, they make pouder of it, and laying a coale of fire upon it, at the other end sucke so long that they fill their bodies full of smoke, till that it commeth out of their mouth and nostrils, even as out of the tonnell of a chimney. They saye that this doth keepe them warme and in health; they never go without some of it aboute them. We ourselves have tryed the same smoke, and having put it into our mothes, it seemed almost as hot as Pepper. . . ."

These then, the bountiful bequests of the Indians to the European farmer: methods of cultivation suited to the soil, the climate, and the primitive agricultural tools available; crops such as corn, beans, pumpkins, potatoes, tomatoes, and several more, which not only fed the first farmers but still today make up half of our farms' production; and the great "money crop"—tobacco.

[1] Edwards, Everett E., *American Agriculture*, U. S. Dept. of Agri. *Yearbook*. 1940
[2] Spinden, Herbert J. *Thank the American Indian*, Sci. Amer. 138: 330-332
[3] Medsger, Oliver P. *Edible Wild Plants*. New York. 1939

[4] Faulkner, Harold U. *American Economic History*. New York. 1924
[5] Josselyn, John. *New England Rarities*. London. 1671
[6] Cartier, Jacques. *A Short and Brief Narration*. In Hakluyt's Voyages. London. 1907
[7] Gray, Asa. *Manual of Botany*, 7th Edition. New York. 1908
[8] Cartier, *ibid*.

CHAPTER IV

THE ENGLISH BACKGROUND OF THE COLONIAL FARMER

LET us look back to an autumn of 1632, and the town of Newbury, Massachusetts.

John Crawford and his young wife, Mercy, stood in the doorway of their new house. Its logs, erected like a palisade but chinked tight against the coming cold by moss, supported a roof of thatch. There were no windows; but the huge fireplace, built of boulders laid in clay from the banks of the near-by Merrimac River, gave light enough. Deerskins, hung curtain-wise, constituted a door. The home was rough and rude, scarcely twelve feet square, but it would serve until there were time and means to build a better one.

The hill behind was felted with a great dark forest of pine and spruce lightened by maples and birch. On either side, its arms closed in around the farm. A rutted track led out to the village toward the shore. Only two scant acres had been cleared, acres studded with fire-blackened stumps, but very well covered with corn and pumpkins not yet harvested.

Farmer John's hands were blistered and his neck was browned to leather by the summer heat. Mercy's hands were roughened, too, but neither the toil they had endured nor the rigors facing them in the years ahead really daunted them.

"I've never before worked so hard nor so long each day," said John, "nor slept so well."

"Aye—slept well, and what's more, in peace," said Mercy. "Very little they'd find in our hut to confiscate!" she added, remembering days of terror in England.

"It's all ours!" John exclaimed, "and our children's— forever more!"

Permanence

In those last words lay the difference between the agriculture of the Indians and the background of the white farmers who settled English America.

The Indian had room enough and to spare and no ties to root him to any particular spot. If his village failed to prosper, it was a simple task to move to the next hill or to go beyond. Within his wide tribal limits the Indian could roam as he pleased. Land to him meant nothing but a hunting-ground, a forest in which his game roamed, and waters in which his fish spawned.

But the white farmer had different ideas. Ownership of a piece of land was his great desire—that and the freedom, the independence, and the security that only land could give. Land, practically valueless to the Indian, was to the white farmer an investment into which he and his family poured their only capital—labor. In proportion to their energy, the value of their estate increased.

The first settlers could never have imagined that subsequent social and industrial developments would cause their descendants to abandon the fields so laboriously cleared from the forest for jobs in mill, factory, or office.

The fields of the colonial farmers, lush with corn, beans, and pumpkins, looked the same as those of the Indians,

but the farmer's field was permanent; that of the Indian was temporary. Therein lay the fatal, basic difference between the old agriculture in America and the new. Against this background European settlers placed their own materials and methods.

Cattle

The first contribution of Europe to American agriculture was the domestic animal. The Indians never tamed a wild creature, save perhaps the dog. Sheep and cattle were importations from Europe. Later, the Plains Indians did make use of the horse, but that valuable creature was in reality an involuntary gift from Europe.

Even if there had been in America the types of animals easily domesticated, it is doubtful if the Indian would have tamed and used them. They were not a pastoral people. Indeed, there were so few Indians about, compared to the vastness of the land, that they had no need of settling down to make the most of limited areas. For example, in the North and East, deer alone were a sufficient source of meat. On the Plains the mighty herds of bison supplied the tribes.

Another reason why domestic creatures were not developed by the Indians was this: the native grasses of America were singularly lacking in nutritive substances. Wild grasses grew abundantly; the sod over the prairies was so heavy that it mocked the first plows; but it was not until the white farmer introduced such fodder plants as the various clovers, and also timothy,[1] that the proper feeding of cattle became possible.[2]

The Indian's sole interest in animals was as a source of meat. For example, in Peru, Spanish settlers in the six-

teenth century introduced camels from the Canary Islands, as beasts of burden.[3] The animals thrived; but, in time, the Spanish abandoned them in favor of horses. Had they been left alive, the camels would have become naturalized and would have prospered. But the Indians, hungry for meat, slaughtered every one of the beasts. The Indian hunger for meat was a mighty source of friction even in the English settlements. All along the frontier, for many generations the redskins persisted in seizing strayed cattle belonging to the colonists and slaughtering them immediately.

Thus the introduction of domestic animals by white farmers was of tremendous importance to the development of American agriculture. The settlers in their tightly packed little ships always managed somehow to find room, not only for their families, but also for cattle, sheep, horses, and poultry.

Besides furnishing meat, eggs, and leather, these creatures supplied wool for clothing; labor for the tilling of the soil; and manure for fertilizing. In those days, animal manure was the only fertilizer available in any quantity.

The farmer with English background was so dependent upon his animals that he brought over more and more of them. Even the Spanish, though at first more interested in gold and religion than in farming, finally did likewise. Columbus in 1493 brought over horses, while in 1494, "50 brace of hens and six roosters" were ferried to the West Indies.[4] Just a year later, another ship brought a cargo of "jennets, jacks, mares, cattle, pigs, sheep, rice, millet, farm laborers, gardeners, a millwright, and a blacksmith."[5]

The English were fully as prompt. The Pilgrims, being almost poverty-stricken, did without cattle for seven years,

EARLY AMERICAN CATTLE MARKET

but Boston settlers, comparatively well-off, furnished their farms adequately with cattle almost from the beginning. In the very first year (1630) thirty cows, twelve mares, and a number of pigs and goats arrived [6]—only a fraction of those originally shipped, for the voyage was as perilous for beasts as for humans. In one shipment of two hundred cattle made by Governor Winthrop to Boston, about seventy died on the high seas.[7]

The importance of animals on the earliest farms can be illustrated by records of the Mason place near Portsmouth, New Hampshire. There, in 1635, an official tax count reported 58 cattle, 92 sheep, 27 goats, 64 swine and 22 horses.[8]

The Dutch about New York, thorough farmers, similarly depended upon cattle, horses, and sheep. They lost no time in shipping livestock to New Amsterdam. From just one expedition arriving at the future city of New York in 1625, a hundred and three domestic animals were received.[9]

Scrub Stock

Usually, the cattle brought over were not of the quality commonly raised today. The modern American farmer would doubtless scorn to support such stock. There were no good cows, sheep, and pigs in that period. Horses were fairly good, for they were important in war and to the gentry. They had been bred with care for generations, ever since the Crusades. But no one bothered to breed cattle and the other farm animals. Such creatures "just happened."

These facts are proven by reports at the Boston market, as late as 1710, of English-bred stock imported for sale.[10]

Weights recorded were: beeves, 370 pounds, calves, 50 pounds; sheep, 28 pounds; lambs, 18 pounds.

Once these runts and scrubs arrived in the New World, the wretched fodder, overwork in the fields, interbreeding, and lack of husbandry still further impoverished them. Peter Kalm wrote in 1748, "Every day their cattle are harassed by labor, and each generation decreases in goodness and size, being kept short of food." [11]

Nevertheless, this importation of livestock marked a great departure of American agriculture from Indian methods. Besides supplying food and clothing, the animals multiplied a farmer's position of strength. They made it possible for him to establish himself securely and to support his family on a scrap of land that would not have supported a single Indian for a month.

Better Farmers

The second extension of the English background (and of the Dutch) was the improvement in methods of farming. Of course, cultivation in the Old World then was still primitive. It was a matter of almost bestial toil for the peasant. Methods were crude, and farming was not dreamed of as a science. It was all a matter of tradition; of rules and superstitions handed down from father to son. By the middle of the seventeenth century, however, there were signs of improvements in European farm methods. Rotation of crops was begun—the so-called "fallow field" system—and the fertilization of fields, long practiced, was more carefully worked out. More important, new crops such as potatoes were introduced; and better implements were being evolved.

The first farmers in America knew little of these inno-

vations. But as the tide of settlement flowed overseas from Europe, and new arrivals leapfrogged westward over the lands of farmers already established, the new ideas and methods also gradually spread. Thus the farmer in America neatly united time and circumstance. From the Old World came new methods at the time most suited for grafting them upon the fluid combination of English background and Indian practices.

The situation is strikingly illustrated in American agricultural geography.

In the Northern English colonies, the rough and rugged individualism of the settlers, mostly poor or middle-class folk, created the small town and the jealously separated farmstead. Both were perfect for New England conditions.

In the Southern area of a far more gracious climate, tobacco and soil conspired with the more aristocratic type of settler to establish large plantations.

In French America, such as Quebec, the French communal type of farming found an ideal and necessary development. The long winters and general poverty made self-help and mutual aid of the community a colonizing method which fitted the conditions as neatly as a glove a man's hand.

In the South, the Spanish found the same arid conditions as at home, plus Indians at hand to serve as slaves or laborers. The Spanish adjusted themselves easily. Irrigation was known back in old Spain. Thus when the Catholic padres arrived at the dry lands of New Mexico and Southern California, they taught the Indians to build irrigation systems. Those at Santa Fe and at several of the California missions are examples.

European Crops Transplanted

Two other contributions to American agriculture came with the New World farmer from his European background. These were crops and tools.

The farmer could subsist with the native plants under cultivation by the Indians, but he had no need to limit himself to such poverty. Corn even at its best is a coarse grain and was then strange to European palates; and the farmer and his family raised other grains beside corn and beans. They soon had fields of wheat, rye, barley, buckwheat, and peas. These were the great staple crops, needed not only for food for the home table, but as cash crops of cereals that could be sent back to England.

Vegetables did not play a large part in the agricultural economy. "Vitamins" were then unknown. For casual home and local use, such things as cabbages, turnips, onions, parsnips, beets, and carrots were brought into production. Doubtless the farm wife raised or gathered greens, too, and encouraged her family to eat salads, though on this subject the historians of the time are silent. The pie plant, rhubarb, however, was in use.

The tomato, where known, as for instance in the Far South, was ignored as a poisonous weed. The potato was also slighted until, having been taken from America[12] and the West Indies to Ireland and Germany, its vast popularity there caused its triumphant return to America.

As for fruits, the farmers lost no time in planting orchards. The Puritans at Boston, for example, promptly set out rows of apple trees, pears, plums, and cherries. Of Boston orchards, Josselyn[13] reported:

"Our fruit trees prosper abundantly. Apple-trees, Peare-trees, Cherry-trees, Plum-trees, Quince-trees,

Barberry-trees. I have observed with admiration that the Kernels sown or the Suckers planted produce as fair and good fruit without grafting, as the Tree from whence they were taken: the Countrie is replenished with faire and large Orchards."

The New England farmer remembered the succulent peaches of Old England and tried to raise them, but the climate was too harsh. Further south, the peach did well, however—as in New Amsterdam.

"If a (peach) stone is put into the earth, it will spring the same season, and grow so rapidly as to bear fruit in the fourth year, and the limbs are frequently broken by the weight of the peaches, which are usually very fine." [14]

Today, we sigh for the days when there were no insect pests or diseases like those which now make the spraying calendar so burdensome. But it is always to be remembered that the fruits themselves, however hardy, were of very poor quality as compared to the modern varieties which are popular today.

The English, Dutch, and French farmers simply transplanted to their New World farms such of their European background plant material as was convenient and valuable. The Spanish, however, not only did this—practically moving Spanish agriculture intact and adding Indian materials—but also were the first deliberately serious plant-hunters and introducers in America.

The stately galleons which crossed to the New World to bring home the looted treasures of the Incas were compelled by law to take seeds and plants westward from Spain and the Canary Islands. Spanish ships sailing eastward from the Philippines to Panama and the west coast of the Americas also imported tropical plants. It is prob-

able that it was the Spaniard who thus introduced the sugar cane and the coconut palm.[15]

Iron Tools

The tools used in farming were the same as were then used in Europe, plus every new tool developed in due time on the new continent.

The great gift of Europe to America was iron—of which the Indian necessarily knew nothing. With iron, agriculture really began. First, there was the rifle, a cumbersome thing in those days. But with it the early farmer proved his title to his land by liquidating the Indian, and with it he in large part fed his family. Then there was the axe, the tool with which the farmer cleared his land, built his home, and cut fuel for his hearth.

After these, the essentially agricultural tools went to work. The spade, the hoe, the scythe, the reaping hook, the harrow, the cart, and the plow—these were the chief tools the farmer brought with him from his original European home.

Josselyn's advice to prospective immigrant farmers, in 1638 [16] illustrates this. He wrote that they should bring: "Five broad hoes, five narrow hoes, five felling axes, two steel hand-saws, two hand-saws, one whip-saw, a file, a saw set, two hammers, three shovels, two spades, two augers, two broad axes, six chisles, three gimblets, two hatchets, two froues to cleave pail, two hand-bills, nails of all sorts, two pick-axes, three locks and a pair of fetters, two currie combs, a brand to brand beasts with, a chain and lock for a boat, a coulter weighing 10 pounds, a hand-vise, a pitch-fork, a hundred-weight of spikes, nails and pins . . . and a share (plowshare) . . ."

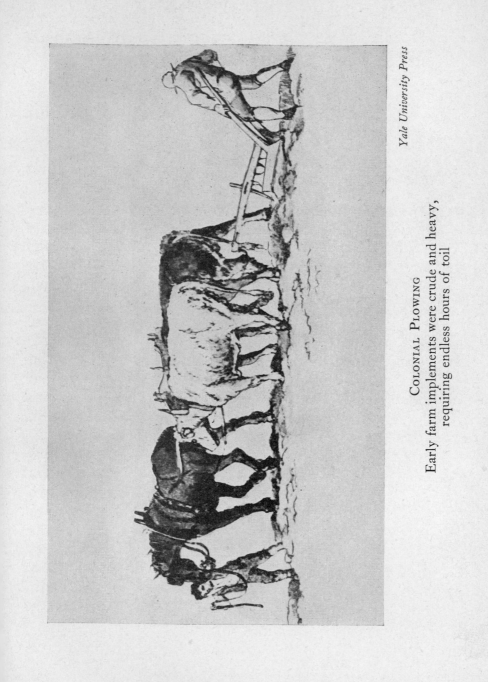

Yale University Press

COLONIAL PLOWING

Early farm implements were crude and heavy,
requiring endless hours of toil

This is purely a literary listing. An actual account of an early farmer's possessions can be obtained from the detailed wills which were filed for probate. From such wills filed in Essex County, Massachusetts, a place then (as now) prosperous in an agricultural way, a writer[17] has assembled the following list as typical: "Bills, broad hoes, carts, colter, dung fork, fans, flail, fork tines, forks, grub-axe, hand bills, harrow tines, harrows, hay knife, hoes, reaping hooks, mattocks, pickaxes, pitchforks, ploughs and ploughirons, rakes, scythes, shovels, sickles, sleds, spades, wheelbarrows, wheels."

Only a prosperous and established farmer could own all of these tools. The plow, for example, the basic agricultural tool, was scarce for many years. These plows, heavy and awkward things, poorly made and very rough-surfaced, were difficult for animals to pull. It took two men (or a man and a boy) using two or three horses or four to six oxen an entire day to plow one to two acres.[18]

Even so, the possession of a plow made a farmer a man of distinction. Often there were only one or two plows in an entire community. Plymouth, Massachusetts, had no plow for the first twelve years. Wealthier Boston had, on the contrary, thirty plows within six years of its settlement. The Swedes in Delaware had few tools of any kind, but the Dutch and William Penn's Quaker and German (later called "Pennsylvania Dutch") tenants in Pennsylvania, had them in abundance.

If the plow was poor, so were nearly all other tools. Indeed, the first farmers in America used methods and tools in planting and harvesting grain, for example, which were comparable to those in use in Palestine 2,000 years before! [19]

The Wheel

Finally, one of the greatest of gifts from the European background was the wheel. Roads were nonexistent in America at first, of course, but even for local hauling on the farm itself, the wheel was one of the greatest single additions to Indian agriculture that the colonist white farmer contributed.

He could watch the Indians (usually the squaw) hauling loads on a hurdle made of two long poles with sticks at the further end for a platform. The Indian woman and her children also carried loads from place to place on their heads or in pack baskets strapped to their backs. In the winter there was the Indian sled and the Indian toboggan. These the farmer readily adopted and still uses.

But in the summer the wheel alone made it possible to carry on farm work. Once the first crude roads were cut, the wheel carried the farm surplus to market and brought home products imported from Europe and the larger American settlements where artisans already had established themselves.

A Nation of Farmers

These, then, were the backgrounds of American agriculture. Bold and fearless men and women, driven by hopeless economic and social conditions of the Old World, where liberty and advancement for themselves were impossible, dared to cross the Atlantic to the New World—because there land was free.

At first, the only way to support a family was to farm, and so the New World became a nation of farmers.

The Indians were successful farmers. From them the white farmer learned methods suited to the soil, climate,

and the primitive conditions. From them he adopted a group of plants of great value and importance. To this Indian heritage he added his European background, namely, permanent possession of his scrap of soil, domestic animals, more efficient methods of production, his own favored plant materials, his more efficient tools—and the wheel, which enlarged his economic field.

[1] Bidwell, P. W. and Falconer, J. I. *History of Agriculture in the Northern United States*, 1620-1860, Washington. 1925

[2] Bordley, John B. *Essays and Notes*, 2nd Ed. Philadelphia. 1801

[3] Cobo, El. P. Barnabe. *Historia del Nuevo Mundo*. Seville. 1890-1895

[4, 5] Navarette, Martin Fernandez. *Coleccion de los Viajes y Deccubrimientos*. 2nd Ed. Madrid. 1859

[6] Higginson, Francis. Journal. In *Young's Chronicles of Mass*. Boston. 1846

[7] Smith, Capt. John. In *Mass. Historical Society's Collections*, 3rd Series, III, 40.

[8] New Hampshire State Records. I, 115

[9] Wassenare, Nicholas van. In Jameson, J. Franklin, *Narratives of New Netherlands*, New York. 1909

[10] Bogart, Ernest L. *Economic History of the American People*. New York. 1935

[11] Kalm, Peter. *Travels Into North America*. London. 1770

[12] Bidwell. *Op. cit.*

[13] Josselyn, John. Mass. Historical Society. *Collections 3rd Series*. III, 337

[14] Van der Donk, Adriaen. *Description of the New Netherland*. In *N. Y. Historical Society Collections*. 2d Series. I, 125-242

[15] Whitaker, Arthur P. *The Spanish Contribution to American Agriculture*. In *Agricultural History* for January, 1929

[16] Josselyn, John. *Mass. Historical Society. Collections*. III, 224

[17] Bidwell. *Op. cit.*

[18, 19] Edwards, Everett E. *American Agriculture, U. S. Dept. of Agriculture, Yearbook*. 1940 et seq.

PART II
THE COLONIAL PERIOD, 1600-1784

As a result, nine out of every ten arrivals became farmers. As Hutchinson wrote of New England,[2] the desire for land was "the ruling passion" of the period; a farm was the sign and symbol of manhood.

But the mere possession of land was only a beginning. The land had to be cleared. A house and barn had to be built. Crops had to be planted, cultivated, and harvested. The farmer facing the task of carving his farm out of the wilderness and then of carrying along the work of the seasons could not accomplish everything with his own hands. Nor could his wife do everything there was to be done inside the four walls of the rough and rude dwelling. They had to have help. The more abundant the help, the more prosperous the farm.

Children were the best way of solving this labor problem. Sons were particularly desired, for they were the hardiest laborers. Daughters were welcome, however; the more the better.

Bondsmen

But the farmer had other sources of labor, for example, the indentured servant or bondsman. There were also unfortunates who had run afoul of the English law and, in lieu of being hanged or confined to a jail, were transported to the Colonies to work out their sentences. Legally these last were felons; but many of them were guilty merely of political crimes.

The indentured servants were men and women—and sometimes children—who wanted to come to America but lacked the fare. In return for passage, supplied by an agent who profited on the deal, they bound themselves to work for five years or more. The agent took them overseas

and there "sold" them into employ. The farmer thus obtained for a small price the services of a man in his fields, and his wife the help of a woman about the house. In return, the farmer provided board, lodging, clothing, and religious opportunity.

In general, the system worked very well. As in Massachusetts, the Great and General Court (the future State Legislature) took pains to see that these bondsmen were not abused. Hours of labor were fixed, and any mistreatment brought heavy fines. In the case of child bondservants, the farmer was obligated to provide time for the child to be educated in the "three R's" at public cost. In many cases the bondsmen became almost members of the family which had bought their time. There was little or no distinction in labor, food, or clothing.

There were, however, flaws in the system which made their appearance after a time. Bondsmen in America talked among one another somewhat as follows:

"We're working too hard," said one, "because there aren't enough of us bondservants to meet the demand. The work is too great in this new country, and the hands are too few."

"Five years is too long a time to be slaving for someone else," said another. "No man with a bone in his back is going to abide his time."

A third worker edged into the conversation. "Opportunities are great around here," he said. "I'm planning to run out. I'll just disappear some dark night and walk into a new neighborhood."

It goes without saying that some of the others followed this man's example. With cash earned as a free farm laborer, the escaped bondsman could march on a little fur-

ther, take up new land, and have a farm of his own. After two years had passed since his escape, the colonial statute of limitations freed a bondservant from his contract, and he could go anywhere he wished without risk of being brought back to work it out.

Indian Workers

In the early days, Indians were forced into slavery as captives taken in war. Others were employed as hired hands. Both methods failed completely, for the Indian was incapable of routine toil. When his own master, he would labor amazingly, often enduring the greatest degree of hunger and cold. But the Indian's was a proud spirit that could never be broken to servitude.

In 1700 Pastoris[3] wrote on this point: "If one of these savages allows himself to be persuaded by a Christian to work, he does it with complaining, shame, and fear, as an unaccustomed act."

Negro Slaves

Of course, in the South, Negro slaves solved the labor problem for the first two centuries, but in the North this was not possible. There were some Negro slaves owned in the New England area (and more of them in New York and Pennsylvania), but they never were of numerical importance. The reason was—they did not pay. Many of the early Negroes could not endure the cold winters. They were so often ill with respiratory troubles and so quickly died that it was foolish from the farmer's point of view to waste money buying such labor. Thus Negro slaves were confined mostly to the larger towns and cities and utilized as servants.

Backbreaking Days

It is small wonder that the Indian and the Negro did not fill the need for farm labor. It is really impossible for us today to realize how endless and backbreaking was the work on the colonial farm. The farmer, his sons, and his hired man worked in the fields, the forest, and the barn. His wife, his daughters, and possibly some other female relatives in need of a home, worked in and around the house. Everyone worked endlessly.

The old Yankee saying stems from this period: "Man's work is from sun to sun, but a woman's work is never done." Housework was not only difficult because of crude and makeshift appliances, but even more so because each household had to be self-sufficient. The colonial farm in the North was the epitome of subsistence agriculture.

The Farm Wife

The farmer's wife not only carried along the routine work of cooking and cleaning, but made cloth and clothes. She took raw wool from the farm's sheep or crude flax from the farm's fields, prepared the fibres, and spun them into threads. She wove them into cloth on the farm loom, usually a heavy, homemade contraption that was hard to operate. She spent some time in the fields and forest, gathering barks with which to dye the wool red, yellow, brown, gray, and black.

From her flock of hens and from the wild fowl her men brought to the table, she saved feathers to make feather beds. Between these the family slept most comfortably during the winter nights. The bedsteads, made by the men of the family, were just head and tail pieces with the mid-

dles filled in with slats of wood or of old cordage woven crisscross.

The farmer's wife brewed the family's beer and ale. She concocted the family medicines, making use of herbs brought over from England and native herbs the Indian squaws had pointed out. She made hooked and braided rugs to cover the plain pine flooring. She pieced bedquilts, and the family candles were her handiwork. Soap was made once a year by boiling together grease saved from cooking and lye made from hardwood ashes taken from the fireplace. In season, the farm wife picked edible berries in the woods. She preserved for winter use the surplus meat, vegetables and fruits from the farm, in such forms as mincemeat, corned beef, salt meat, salt fish, and sun-dried apples.

It was the farm woman who made the home. In a multitude of ways she made life possible and added what comfort, beauty, and grace the poverty and narrow circumstances of the wilderness allowed. Her only recreation was the community life she shared with other women at infrequent quilting bees, harvest suppers, and the like. Probably the only regular leisure she enjoyed was in sitting absolutely still during the three-and four-hour-long sermons preached in the local church.

Marriage, the condition she accepted as a matter of course, was in itself a sentence to a life term of hard labor. She merely exchanged the status of an unpaid hand in her mother's household for that of a wife in her husband's home, with even more work and the added burden of childbearing. Nine and more often ten children in a family were common. Many a wornout wife found rest in an early grave.

The gravestones of the old New England cemeteries tell the story. Many a stone gives the name of the father of a family and his age, often the full Biblical three-score and ten. Under his name are the names and ages of his wives —the first, married at sixteen or seventeen, died at twenty-five to thirty; the second, often again not much more than a child, repeated the fifteen-year term; while the third, whom he married at his middle age, commonly outlived him. Women were not only valuable but scarce in the colonial period, and no maid or widow was long permitted to enjoy the single state.

The Farmer's Life

The farmer and his sons enjoyed a somewhat brighter lot. They sometimes fished and hunted. This must have provided many a happy interval of escape from the daily round of toil. And the men entered into the life of the community—Indian wars, militia drill, town meetings, community activities of many kinds.

But only for short periods did the farmer escape the crushing load of manual labor. Agriculture in the North was made possible only by calloused hands and aching backs. So crushing was the labor required to extort a living from the stony soil of the North, especially in New England; and so meagre were the returns from the soil itself; that when fertile acres of the Ohio and beyond were publicized, New England farms were gladly abandoned in an astonishing number. Witness the fact that there are a million fewer acres of land in cultivation today, in Massachusetts alone, than in 1810.[4]

Epitome of the farmer's early toil in New England are the prevalent stone walls. Some exist today, marking the

boundaries between farms and separating pastures from woodlots. They also wind their way, crumbling and fallen, through forests a hundred years old, trees that have grown since the fields were forsaken. Often such a mossy wall, buttressed by ferns, is the only remainder of some colonial homestead.

This preliminary toil of getting rid of the stones was hard enough, but the routine cultivation also entailed endless endeavor. The farmer, when he was wealthy enough to own a plow, still had a very poor and rough instrument. Commonly, all he purchased was the metal share. The rest of the tool he made himself, just as he made his hayrake and many other tools.

Plowing was desperately hard work. These early plows were so heavy that the farmer usually provided them with wheels. Peter Kalm wrote of them:[5] "The wheels upon which the plough beam is placed are as thick as the wheels of a cart, and all the woodwork is so clumsily made that it requires a horse to draw the plough along a smooth field."

The farmer's axe and hatchet were not much different from those in use today, although heavier and less smoothly finished. But such tools were expensive; and in general the farmer looked to wood for almost everything else he needed. He sat before the fire on winter nights and with busy knife and drawshave made his wooden-toothed rakes and harrows, his axe and hammer handles, his snathe for his scythe, and other farm tools. He also made wooden bowls and spoons for the table, wooden spinning wheels, looms, and other appliances which his wife needed about the house.

A good example of the dependence of the colonial

farmer upon his own muscles is his method of harvesting grain. For reaping he used the sickle. To cut the grain he had to bend his back and swing his arm all day long. He might possibly reap as much as a half-acre in that twelve-hour day. After the harvest was in, he threshed the grain on the barn floor by swinging a flail. To winnow out the chaff, he tossed the grain into the air until the wind had cleaned it. This was all hand labor.

Not only were tools for the most part poor, crude makeshifts, but added to the great labor required to produce a crop was the wasteful and inefficient method of farming itself. Agriculture was in a large degree a hit-or-miss affair. Even with good soil, results were poor. To obtain a sufficiently large crop, the farmer had to cultivate more soil and work much longer and more strenuously than he would have found necessary had he been a better agriculturist.

For example, instead of keeping true to the two-or-three-field system as on the European continent, where a field lay fallow every second or third year, the colonial farmer practiced what amounted to the one-field system. Once he had cleared a field, he planted it until the yield fell far off. Then he used the field for cattle pasturage, and hacked and burned a new field out of the woods. This meant hard labor and poor crops, once the virgin soil had been drained of its fertility.

No less a person than George Washington deplored this habit of the farmers. In 1791[6] after his Presidential tour of the seaboard, he wrote: "The Aim of the farmers in this country, if they can be called farmers, is not to make the most of the land which is, or has been cheap, but the most of the labour, which is dear; the consequence of which

has been, much ground has been scratched over and none cultivated or improved as it ought to have been; whereas a farmer in England, where land is dear, and labour cheap, finds it in his interest to improve and cultivate highly, that he may reap large crops from a small quantity of ground."

The Magic Wand of Trade

Had the English colonies remained purely agricultural, the course of history must have been different than it was. A pastoral people would scarcely have been strong enough to win independence. But while the farmer was establishing himself along the coast and pushing his way westward (new settlers moving past the farms previously established), the colonies also were developing very fast commercially.

The contrast between the Spanish and the English colonies makes this clear. Spain had a deliberate colonial policy. She gave practical encouragement both to settlement and to agriculture. The British crown did not. As a result, in the early days, the colonies of Spain in America[7] were much more prosperous than were the original Thirteen Colonies of England.

The Spanish area of America, however, remained purely agricultural; whereas the future United States, spurred by necessity and unhampered by the Crown, developed foreign trade. This was particularly true of New England. The Yankees were literally compelled to look to the sea for prosperity. Fish, forest products, and agricultural surpluses were staples which the West Indies and the Old World needed.

The development of trade, romantic as any chapter

in American history,[8] resulted in a new life for many colonists. It is significant to agriculture because the farmer was himself benefited. Not only did the ships provide a market for his production, but the same ships brought back cargoes which enlightened his life and provided him with more and better tools. Most important of all, trade brought new ideas which made him a better citizen as well as a better farmer.

The Farmer's House

The houses in which the farmers lived demonstrate this gradual development of agriculture as a result of the wealth developed by foreign trade. The farmers lived for the first year or two in rude shacks. Sometimes they were but holes dug into a convenient hillside and faced against the weather by a palisade of logs. Usually a temporary shack was soon followed by a crude log cabin, a small one-room affair, windowless and roofed with sod or birch bark. The floor was the earth itself; and the huge fireplace, made of stone mortared with mud or clay, had a chimney constructed of sticks smeared with mud. Such a house was neither comfortable nor sanitary, but it furnished fairly good protection against the weather.

This log cabin was replaced later on with a decent house made of sawn sheathing fastened over a frame of timbers hewn from trees on the place. Wood was cheap and abundant, and the frames were solidly mortised together. Many of these old houses still stand today, so strongly were they built. After a time, bricks were available for chimney construction; and the wealthier families erected homes of brick. Glass was scarce and expensive, but it

gradually came into use, replacing the oiled paper and the scraped deerskins formerly used for windowpanes.

In general, farmhouses followed two types, both severely plain and simple, not from choice but through necessity. They were truly functional and as such established an excellent, native architectural style.

The first type was a low building of one story or one and a half, with four rooms in the main block, two rooms in the "attic," and the kitchen in an ell. It is now miscalled the "Cape Cod cottage."

The second type was much larger and created somewhat later because of the need of housing large families. It was two or two and a half stories high, with four rooms in a block in each of the two main stories and with the attic usually unfinished. Sometimes the kitchen was in an added ell of either one or two stories, although often the kitchen was one of the main block rooms. Usually, the house was tied in with the outbuildings by means of a woodshed which made a covered passage from house to barn. Thus the farm family could do the winter work secure from storm and cold.

Fireplaces

The farmers paid careful attention to the chimney. This was usually a noble stack of brick erected on a foundation of field stone, often in massive blocks. These chimneys contained the great fireplace flues. Fireplaces were the only means of heating the houses and of cooking until about 1850, when stoves began to become common.

The kitchen fireplace was commonly the largest. A man could stand upright in one of them, and it would take logs so large that a man could not lift one of them alone. It

was not remarkable for a horse to be used to drag a back-log into the house and for the massive bulk of timber then to be levered and rolled into the fireplace.

This great kitchen hearth was the center of the home for the farmer and his family. Often even in the coldest weather the rest of the house was unheated. But in the kitchen the fire always burned. Massive wooden settles usually flanked the fireplace. The farmer and his wife seated themselves on stools or the butts of logs in front of the flames. Romping children camped outside the ring of their elders, managing very well with what heat sifted through.

Inside the fireplace, iron cranes swung on pivots fastened to the bricks. From S-hooks hung on these cranes dangled iron and copper pots filled with savory stews of venison, bubbling corn-meal mush, or other foods. Tin ovens, artfully arranged to concentrate the heat of the fire into their centers, served as bake ovens and as means of keeping the meals hot until they were served.

Hung from pegs driven into the ceiling rafters were hams, sides of bacon, and festoons of sausages. There were also ropes of dried apples and bunches of rue, bergamot, boneset, mint, and other herbs and "simples" used by the housewife to season her meals, to brew "teas," to blend salves, and to make blood purifiers and other medicines of the day.

Mows were filled with hay and grain. Cattle, pigs, hens, and horses occupied the barn. Cellars were crowded with fruits and vegetables and barrels of cider and crocks of mincemeat, salted beef, and pork; while the pantries were packed with wheat flour, corn meal, and other foods.

Life was hard, toil was endless, but this subsistence

farming was a way of life that developed the men who
stood at Lexington and Concord and went on to win national independence.

Farm homes during the past 150 years have changed. In
particular, given electricity, a farmhouse now can have
about all the comforts and conveniences of a city apart-
ment—and many advantages which the city does not offer.

Barns

It is a different matter with the barns of today. They are
scarcely changed from those of colonial times, at least in
New England.

The farmer of three hundred years ago developed a
regular system for providing himself with a barn. In mid-
winter, once the next year's firewood was cut, he and his
sons first cut down great oaks or pines. Then with axe and
adze they hewed the timbers into foot-square sills, scarcely
smaller posts, plates, rafters, and studding. Each member
of the barn was made with a tenon to fit the mortise cut in
the proper place of another member.

"Shape those joints carefully," the farmer would ad-
monish his bondservant. "They must fit so well that each
joint would pinch a hair!"

"That's going to a lot of trouble," the bondsman might
reply.

"Aye, but for a reason," was the inevitable response.
"We can't have a slipshod job. I'm building this barn not
just for myself, but for my sons and their sons forever."

This done, the farmer issued a call to his neighbors, ap-
pointing a day for a barn-raising bee. It was a civic duty
for the community to respond. The men fell to work with
rope and tackle. Once the sills were dragged into place on

HUSKING CORN IN OLD NEW ENGLAND

the stone foundation blocks, the posts were erected. In a few hours the frame of the great barn was up, each joint securely fastened with a wooden peg driven through—a barn fifty by a hundred feet in size.

Meanwhile, the womenfolk were baking pies and breads, roasting meats, boiling puddings and vegetables. The minute the sun's shadow told of noon, a cowhorn would be blown, and the men, after a hasty douse in well or spring water, rushed to the table. The hearty fare was washed down with copious drafts of rum. That liquor had come to be the masculine beverage of New England, once the slave and molasses trade started the Yankee distilleries going full blast. A gallon of the fiery stuff cost but a shilling. So popular was the drink that it was part of a farmhand's wages—a pint a day.

Usually a single community working day was enough to frame a barn. Then, at their leisure, the farmer and his sons would sheath the building, using lumber sawed from their own trees, usually at the local water-power mill. Pine was the lumber for sheathing; and the great trees of the day furnished huge boards of remarkable width— often up to four feet.[9] For shingles, the farmer himself split soft pine or cedar into "shakes," which were similar to our modern shingle, but much larger as a rule and irregular in size and thickness. Thus the building's exterior was completed. It was seldom painted—new sheathing being cheaper than paint.

Inside, the entire center was left open to the roof. Rows of stalls were usually run down each side for cattle and horses and, when the need arose, a scaffold of poles was placed across the barn between the stall tops to make a flooring for the hay which was heaped in overhead.

Here is a description of a haymow in a Colonial barn:[10]
". . . on the scaffold over the stables the 'horse hay'
was garnered, and upon the 'little scaffold' over the far
end of the barn floor were nicely piled the bound sheaves
of wheat, rye, or barley, the butts all placed outward to
hinder the entrance of mice. Over the great beams were
scaffolds made of round poles and pieces of waste lumber,
generally in such a condition as to make a first class man-
trap. On this scaffold was heaped the crop of oats, all
awaiting the thrashing flail, the use of which generally
began about Thanksgiving time. Who, raised on a farm,
does not remember the miseries of the boy who stowed
away the hay about the time the mow hole was filled, and
pitching over the great beams commenced?"

Flailing, now a farm chore gratefully forgotten, was
one of the early winter chores faced by every farm family.
There were mills, usually water-powered (although
sometimes windmills were built) to grind the grain; but
at first the farmer himself had to beat out the grain from
the sheaves which he cut and bound in the field in August
and September.

A hard, smooth floor was laid in a section of the barn,
and there the sheaves were spread, waiting to be threshed.
The flail consisted of two bars of wood united by a hinge.
One bar, rounded, was the handle; the other, a flat one,
was the beater. How that tool blistered the hands! How
backs ached from a day of "thrashing"! And how the dust
rasped the throat!

Sometimes horses or even oxen were used, in true Biblical manner, to tread out the grain. The following describes
such a practice in Rhode Island:[11]

"When a barley heap is to be thrashed, previous care

is taken to have it placed on a hard, level floor. A quantity of barley in the sheaf is then laid in a circular train to be trampled upon by horses. Sometimes three or four horses are ridden round upon the barley by boys; at other times a man stands in the center of the circle and, with the reins in one hand and a whip in the other, drives two or three pairs of young horses round upon the barley, whilst another person is employed with a rake to turn the barley and expose it properly to the action of the horses' feet. When the grain of one layer is thoroughly beaten from the straw, the latter is raked into a heap without the circle and the former into a heap within."

Foursquare with the World

Too much emphasis cannot be given to this fact: the subsistence type of farming made the early settlers self-sufficient, cost what it might in toil, and narrow as were the circumstances of life. The farmer and his family stood foursquare with the world. They produced by their labor from the forest and the field almost everything they needed—not food alone, but clothing, furniture, drugs, liquor, and even the tools with which they worked.[12]

The farmer and his family wore clothes of their own making—shoes of leather from their own cattle; linen shirts from their own flax; woolen coats and dresses from the fleeces of their own sheep; straw hats braided from their own wheat straw; and winter caps of racoon skins their own young sons had procured. When the farmer slept at night he rested on the feathers of his own fowl or of wild birds he had shot for the table. Blankets, sheets, pillowcases, quilts—they were all homemade, as were the tablecloths and towels.

The farmer's horses and oxen were harnessed with lines cut from hides of his own cattle. The yoke he carried about his shoulders, when gathering pails of maple sap for sugar, and the yoke his oxen wore in plowing a field—both were completely his own products, save for the iron rings and staples. Every tool he used was fitted with a handle he had whittled from ash shoots.

"How little he bought and how much he contrived to supply his wants by home manufacture would astonish this generation." [13]

The farmer's food in particular was nearly all his own. "The ordinary food of the farmer's family, although abundant, was of the simplest, demanding the sauce of a good appetite and sound digestive powers. Tables 'groaned,' but chiefly under the weight of 'bean porridge hot and bean porridge cold'; brown bread, hominy or hasty pudding and milk; pork, salt beef; boiled, salt, and fresh fish; succotash; and the commoner vegetables in season. Molasses and honey sufficed for sweetening, sugar being costly . . ." [14]

Many a farmer also had maple sugar for sweetening and confections. He had mincemeat; his own wheat flour for bread; butter, cheese, and cream from his cows; apples, pears, plums, and berries; and all the cider and perry (pear juice) he could desire; and as much beer and ale and even whiskey as he cared to brew and distill.

Tea and coffee were scarce and very dear, but there was plenty of meat. The farmer had his own hams and bacon, his own roast beef, lamb, and pork, wild ducks, turkeys, swans, and pigeons—not to omit trout, bass, perch, and salmon; and, if he lived near salt water, cod, haddock, halibut, clams, oysters, and lobsters. At first, sea

food was so plentiful that the gathering was usually the chore of children.

Off the Farm

And it must also be made clear that, despite his endless round of chores, daily and seasonal, most farmers somehow found time for other work. Along the coast, the men and boys went fishing in the winter. When farm work slackened a little and the women could attend to it, the farmer sometimes hired himself out as a temporary shipbuilder in one of the many shipyards that filled every cove along the Atlantic shore with the clatter of mallets and the chipping of adzes.

Inland, and also along shore, the farmer also hired himself out for other special work for which he might have either a talent or the extra time and strength. He might work for a while as a carpenter, a stone mason, a butcher, a stone-wall builder, a shingle splitter, or a lumberman.

Usually the farmer, save in the towns, did not work for wages. He took his pay in salt, iron, or some other staple he needed at home on the farm. He might even exchange his time for some dainty silk or English woolen to please his wife or daughters; and always he was anxious to obtain gunpowder and lead to mould into bullets.

This early colonial type of subsistence farming was created not by poverty alone but by the lack of a market.[15] But in time markets did open, as foreign trade sprang up. Also, as cities (like Boston) developed, they afforded local markets for foodstuffs.

Thus colonial agriculture prospered. The early products the farmer took to market illustrate the basis of this

agricultural economy in the North. Newspaper advertisements read: "Wanted: pot or pearl ashes, whiskey, wheat, pork, lard, butter, rye, corn, oats, flax, timothy seed, clover seed, bees wax, tallow, etc."[16] In exchange, manufactured goods, such as tools and gunpowder brought from England, were offered.

The habit of self-sufficiency, nurturing a rugged independence, persists even today. Back in New England, the old habit of "eat it up; make it do; wear it out; do without" still endures, an inheritance that is three hundred years old.

[1] Franklin, Benjamin. *Works.* Sparks Edition. Philadelphia. 1840
[2] Hutchinson, Thomas. *History of Massachusetts Bay.* Boston. 1767
[3] Pastoris, Francis D. *Circumstantial Geographical Description.* In Mayers, Albert C. *Narratives.* New York. 1912
[4] Massachusetts State Census of 1935
[5] Kalm, Peter. *Travels Into America.* London. 1771
[6] Washington, George. *Letters on Agriculture to Arthur Young and Sir John Sinclair.* 1791
Franklin Knight Edition. Washington. 1847
[7] Whitaker, Arthur P. *Spanish Contribution, Agricultural History,* January, 1929
[8] Clark, William H. *Ships and Sailors, A History of the American Merchant Marine.* L. C. Page & Co. Boston. 1936
[9] Such four-foot-wide boards may be seen today in the old town house at Washington, N. H. (author's measurement).
[10] Thompson, Francis M. *History of Greenfield, Mass.* Greenfield. 1904
[11] Massachusetts Historical Society. *Collections, 1st Series* IX, 200
[12] Bidwell and Falconer. *Op. cit.*
[13] Hedges, Henry P. *Development of Agriculture in Suffolk County.* New York. 1885
[14] Nourse, Henry S. *History of Harvard, Massachusetts.* Harvard. 1894
[15] Bidwell and Falconer. *Op. cit.*
[16] Hedrick, Ulysses P. *History of Agriculture in New York.* 1933

CHAPTER VI

THE MIDDLE COLONIES: FATTER ACRES

THE farmer in the colonies between New England and the Potomac River had relatively an easier time of it than his brother in the North. The soil was richer, the climate milder, and the rivers provided smooth highways into the interior. The Yankee had small lands, cramped among the hills and sown with boulders; but the land of the farmer farther south was open, level, and rich with deep topsoil.

The English farmer in the Middle Colonies rubbed elbows with Dutch, Swedish, French, Scotch-Irish, and German-Dutch farmers. Each nationality had individual farming methods to contribute to the others.

These farmers held title to their lands upon a different basis than did those in the North—at least theoretically. Excepting the claims of the Dutch and the Swedes, which came to nothing, ownership of all the land in English America rested in the King. In general, as settlement developed, this land passed into the hands of the farmers in three legal ways—and also in one manner that was distinctly extra-legal.

The First Legal Way

In New England the disposal of the land was marked by conspicuous community action together with a most remarkable disregard of the profit motive.[1] The story is

69

involved; essentially, the Crown gave grants of land to trading Companies, but not to individuals. (An exception was the Gorges Grant in Maine in 1639—but that was unimportant.) To encourage settlement, these Companies granted areas of land to groups of reliable persons. With these grants went an amazing amount of self-government. In effect, each group became a corporation.[2]

For example, suppose a number of families wanted to take possession of land lying beyond the edge of the settlements. The families concerned asked the General Court (the Massachusetts Legislature), which was the agent for the parent Company in London, for permission to migrate there. The General Court ordered a survey both of the area of land and of the character of the would-be settlers. If both were favorable, the grant of land was made.

There were plenty of strings tied to the gift. The new corporation, which is better known as the "town," had to set aside a definite section in a favorable central site for an open space called a Common. About the Common were set apart lots for a church, a school, a market, a burying ground, a minister's house, and a meeting house. Each member of the town was given a house lot of ample size. Houses to a certain number had to be built within a specified time, depending upon circumstances; and so had the civic buildings and a road to link the new settlement with some older one nearest.

This done, the entire town was surveyed, divided into blocks, and distributed by lot in such a manner that each farmer received his share of good blocks as well as his share of the poorer ones.

"It's a good plan," said a farmer of that day. "Everyone is treated alike. Nobody profits by the sale of unoccupied

lands; and they aren't worth a hoot until human lives have been sweated into the acres."

"Right you are," said his neighbor. "It makes land easy to acquire and gives absolute security of title. I own my land. No one can ever take it away from me or charge me any rent."

The Second Legal Way

In sharp distinction, proprietors to the south of New England tried to establish the manorial or feudal system. The Dutch made this effort deliberately. A large tract of land was given to every head of a family who brought fifty people with him to New Netherlands.[3] With the land went the title of "patroon" and the rights and privileges of a feudal lord. Every person on the estate lived under the rule of the patroon.

Many such estates endured for years. But other settlers, especially those who were not Dutch, ignored the patroons successfully, especially after the English seized New York in 1664.

The farmers themselves recognized very soon that the manorial system had a serious fault.

"The patroon couldn't possibly live without us," they told each other. "He depends entirely upon revenue from us farmers."

"Let's move out," the boldest would suggest. "There's a lot of other land available. We don't have to carry this degrading yoke."

Thus in time the manorial system among the Dutch settlers collapsed.

In New Jersey and Delaware the manorial idea was attempted after the Swedes were ousted and the Duke of

York divided the area between his two friends, Lord Berkeley and Sir George Carteret. As a final resort, the would-be lords of the manors attempted to compromise with the independent farmers by charging quitrents—that is, payments which discharged annually all feudal charges, dues, and services.[4] But the farmers balked at quitrents, too. As a result, there was a series of disorders which appeared intermittently until the Revolution ended all manorial pretensions.[5] Most of the manors vanished because of their own economic instability. It was, after all, labor and not land that was most important in the New World's economics.

Pennsylvania began as the private property of the Penn family. The Penns sold titles to settlers, when they could collect the money. The Penns' sale of lands in the legal sense continued for many years; and again it was the Revolution, plus various preceding acts of the Pennsylvania local government, that ultimately abolished the proprietorship.

The Third Legal Way

The third legal way in which a farmer obtained his land, as in Virginia, was by means of the so-called "headright." Every man who came to Virginia was entitled to his share of the Company's property—which was land. He was given fifty acres as his headright. But it soon developed that a man could get the fifty-acre headright for every person he brought to Virginia! (This system prevailed throughout most of the Southern colonies.)

As long as the extension of the headright was confined to a farmer's wife and children, his household servants, and his accompanying relatives, it could be defended. It

CHURNING BUTTER IN THE COLONIAL FARMHOUSE

also was considered ethical for indentured servants to have their fifty-acre headright when their time expired.

But soon fraud entered the picture.

"I tell you it's not right," whispered a colonist to several companions as they stood on a quay watching the unloading of two shiploads of servants and slaves. "The captains of those boats are claiming headrights on each voyage, not only for themselves, but for each of their sailors and each of the passengers!"

"What's to prevent anyone whose business takes him back and forth between Virginia and England from doing the same?" came the question.

And again the reply was, "Not a thing. And anyone who travels along the coast between Boston or New York and the Virginias can do it."

Squatters

The fourth, the "extra-legal" method of a farmer's acquiring land, was simply that of the squatter. This has always been a popular American method of taking up land. The philosophy of the squatter was extremely simple and practical.

"I'm taking this piece of idle land because I like it, and because it has nobody living on it. It doesn't matter whose it really is. I'm settling here."

Rightful owners of wild land were rather glad to have it settled. They looked forward to some vague time in the future when they would ask the squatter to vacate the land or pay for it. To their surprise, the squatter's ownership to the land he had cleared and lived upon became established by the passage of time. Squatters were not, in colonial times, at all unpopular, for in the regions where

squatting flourished, the lands were largely owned by absentee landlords. Squatters in general made good citizens, particularly as they were universally hardy and vigorous souls, who could shoot straight.

Of course, squatters' titles could always be questioned, and they furnished colonial America with much discord, even into the eighteenth century. In 1769 blanket legislation finally confirmed the squatters in permanent ownership of their farms.

The extent of squatting is not appreciated in these days when such free land no longer exists. For one example, by 1726, some 100,000 squatters were in possession of about two thirds of the 670,000 settled acres in Pennsylvania.[6]

Despite the trouble over quitrents and the prevalence of squatting, the fact is that the manorial and the proprietory systems of selling or renting titles were not at all rigorous. Suppose you wanted a farm for yourself in New Jersey. In 1664[7] the proprietors of that colony would give you as a freeman 150 acres; plus 150 acres more for every servant you brought over. In return you paid them a half-penny an acre as a quitrent!

Or suppose you wanted a farm in Penn's Woods. Here is William Penn's own offer:[8] "My conditions will relate to three sorts of people; 1st, Those that will buy; 2dly, Those that take up land on rent; 3dly, Servants. To the first. . . . I shall be certain as to any number of Acres; that is to say, every one shall contain 5,000 acres, free from any Indian encumberance, the price 100 pounds, and for quit-rent but one English shilling or the value of it yearly for 100 acres . . . To the second sort, that take up Land on rent, they shall have liberty to do so, paying yearly one penney per acre, not exceeding 200 acres. To the third

twenty; girls between fourteen and sixteen. After the marriage ceremony, the bride and groom simply moved out beyond a frontier and carved out their farm from the fringe of the wilderness.

It was a rude life at first, but very soon that which had been a frontier became graced with a swelling volume of amenities. The farmer had ways of increasing his income. From the woods he obtained furs, lumber, game, tanning bark, and pearl ash—to list the most important.

Colonial Lumbering

As for lumber, the farmer in the Middle sections, like his counterpart in the North, at first hewed down trees and chipped them into timber with his adze or split them into shakes (shingles). He might, if accomplished, make barrel staves, too. All these sold readily, if it was possible to freight them to market. This was easy if he lived near a navigable stream. It was very difficult if he did not, for what roads existed were merely muddy or dusty tracks. In the winter, of course, there was snow, and great weights of material were hauled on sleds.

Soon sawn timber began to be marketed. The first tool was the whipsaw, a laborious contrivance. Then the settlers developed water-powered mills and Dutch windmills, and this particular burden was taken from the farmer's shoulders. Stream sawmills did not develop until 1860, nor was the circular saw known then. The familiar log-carriage, which runs the log back and forth into the saw, was also unknown. Instead, the saw, a long blade, was pulled up and down into a pit by means of a reciprocating mechanism powered by a water wheel of crude design.

These saws, being very thick, were wasteful of wood

and of time. Probably the average sawmill did not produce more than 1000 board feet a day.[15] Nevertheless they
supplied the timber and the boards from which America
was built, and they gave the farmer a dependable cash
outlet for his logs.

Pearl Ash

The great cash crop of New York, New Jersey, and
Pennsylvania was pearl ash. Wood is rich in the salts of
potassium, vital in the making of soap and other products.
Until about 1860, when mineral deposits of potassium
were first worked, the forests of the world were the only
sources of these salts. Essentially, pearl ash was a by-product of American agriculture. Just burning away the trees
to clear the land provided much ash, and the fireplaces in
farmers' cabins and homes provided more.

The process was elementary. The ashes were collected
and were mixed with water. This solution of the salts was
then boiled away until evaporated. When crude, this salt
was known as "black ash." Refined somewhat, it was
known as "white ash" or "pearl ash." Every farmer had
his pearl-ash kettle.

The volume of this by-product is indicated by the fact
that during the years just after 1800, New York State
alone produced about $300,000 worth annually.[16]

Since it was light in weight, it was easily transported to
market. A man could pack a hundred pounds of it on his
back through rough country. A hundredweight was worth
about ten dollars in cash at the Montreal market,[17] where
most of upstate New York's pearl ash was gathered for
shipment to Europe. Unfortunately, as roads improved

and the trading organization reached out to the remotest farms, production became so great that the price fell.

The fur trade, so far as the farmer was concerned, rapidly declined in importance as settlement multiplied. Animals became scarcer, and professional hunters and traders went on into the wilderness ahead of the farmer. Still, the farmer continued for years to derive some income from animals hunted and trapped near home.

Farmhouses of Brick

The farmer in New England and in New York particularly depended upon wood entirely for his home. In Pennsylvania, Delaware, and Maryland wood was also widely used for buildings. But thanks to the German-Dutch influence, brick and stone soon became the common material out of which many permanent farm structures were built.

The Pennsylvania Dutch, so-called (they were really Pennsylvania Germans), very early in their settlement built potteries and brickyards. They turned out earthenware and bricks which were of such superior quality that many pieces are still in use today. Tiles were also made, and these are even now used in industry, for the early potters worked so well that their tiles are prized as linings for modern kilns. The old tiles stand heat as well as the most modern fire brick, or even better.

The houses were well designed, being freely drawn copies of Dutch and German houses adapted to American needs. Distinguishing features of these frequently imposing homes were arched cellars, spacious hallways, easy flights of stairs, oak-paneled partitions, windows hung

on balancing weights, and open fireplaces in nearly all of the rooms.[18]

Stoves, often made of tiles, were in common use early in the colonial period; and thus the Middle Atlantic farmer enjoyed a greater degree of comfort than his Northern brother. Because of the economy of fuel in stoves, he had less work to do in chopping wood with which to warm his house.[19]

Switzer Barns

One of the most distinctive farm structures in the Pennsylvania Dutch section was the so-called "Switzer" barn. The farmers reared great, solid structures which are still in use today. These great barns form a striking element in the landscape.

A description of these barns reads: ". . . built mostly of stone. On the ground floor are stalls in which their horses and oxen are fed with hay, cut-straw and rye meal; but not always their other beasts. Roots are seldom given to their livestock, being too little thought of. The second floor, with the roof, contains their sheaves of grain, which are thrashed on this floor. A part of their hay is also stored here. Loaded carts and wagons are driven in on this second floor; with which the surface of the earth is there level; or else a bridge is built up to it, for supplying the want of height in the bank, the wall of one end of the house being built close to the bank of a hill cut down . . . The roof is the most costly part of the buildings; but it costs no more to cover three or four stories than one . . ."[20]

This excellent type of barn is typical of the care the Pennsylvania Dutch (Germans) gave their livestock. The farmer in this region stood almost alone in colonial times

in treating his animals decently. It was this same farmer who developed the so-called artificial meadow. These were fields which were planted to such good forage crops as red clover, timothy, and other European grasses, as these plants were much superior in food value to native American forage.[21]

In contrast with the Pennsylvania farmer and his care of his animals, the rest of colonial America was actually brutal. The farmer elsewhere gave his cattle almost no shelter at all and paid scant heed to feeding them. In time, the farmer in the North realized how great his losses were because of the cold winters, and he eventually provided adequate shelter and food for his beasts. Some of the Middle Atlantic States lagged behind in this program, and in the South nothing much was done. Many cattle and pigs run wild in the South to this day.

[1] Akagi, Roy H. *The Town Proprietors of the New England Colonies, etc.* Philadelphia. 1924

[2] Edwards, Everett E. U. S. Department of Agriculture has compiled an extensive bibliography on American Colonial Agriculture. Contrib. 33. 1938

[3] Carman, Kimmel, and Walker. *Historic Currents etc.* Philadelphia. 1938

[4] Bond, Beverly W. Jr. *The Quitrent System in America.* New Haven. 1919

[5] Jameson, John F. *The American Revolution, etc.* Princeton. 1926

[6] Bellaugh, James C. *The Land System.* American Historical Assn. Rpt. New York. 1897

[7] Smith, Samuel. *History of New Jersey.* Burlington. 1765

[8] Hazzard, Samuel. *Annals of Pennsylvania.* Philadelphia. 1850

[9, 10] Beard, Charles and Mary. *Basic History of the United States.* New York. 1944

[11] Irving, Washington. *Wolfred's Roost.*

[12] Irving, Washington. *Legend of Sleepy Hollow.*

[13, 14] Hedrick, U. P. *History of Agriculture in New York.* New York. 1933

[15, 16, 17] Hedrick, U. P. *Op. cit.*

[18] Ellis and Evans, *History of Lancaster County, Penn.* Philadelphia. 1883

[19] Bidwell, etc. *Hist. of Agriculture in the Northern United States. Op. cit.*

[20] Bordley, John B. *Essays and Notes, etc.* Philadelphia. 1801

[21] Shryock, Richard H. *Pennsylvania Germans in American History. Penn. Mag.* 1939

CHAPTER VII

VIRGINIA: TOBACCO AND LUXURY

IT WAS autumn in Virginia in 1650. A red brick mansion house stood upon a knoll, set among gracious oaks not yet colored by the season. Stables, barns, and the cabins of slaves flanked the building. Roses were still flowering in the gardens, and through the open windows came the sounds of busy household activity.

But the center of the day's bustle lay down at the river's edge, where a ship was berthed at the narrow plantation wharf. Its sails were loosed, and an anchor had been dropped in midstream to warp the vessel out into the tide. The crew was hoisting aboard the last of the cargo of great hogsheads which Negro slaves rolled from the barn. Each one was filled with tightly wedged tobacco leaves. Some 30,000 pounds were bound overseas to England—the year's production of the plantation. Down in the cabin the master of the farm gave last instructions to the captain. He spoke of wines he wanted, of certain silks and satins, of a list of books.

"Get me also," said the Virginian, "a stock and a coat, a waistcoat, breeches, shoes—whatever the fashionable bucks are wearing in London. Bring it all back next fall."

The farmer in Virginia and in economically appended sections of Maryland had time to think of fashion. He was faced with an entirely different set of problems than was

the farmer to the North. One plant, a wild weed of the Americas, made a vast gulf between the two sections. That weed was tobacco.

Generalities are unjust, even after three hundred years, but the Virginia farmer was neither a religious refugee nor a poverty-stricken laborer. He has been accused of being the Cavalier type, the aristocrat. That accusation is hardly justified, but it is true that many of the first settlers in the section were of the minor nobility. Many of them were wealthy and active enough to gather for themselves huge tracts of land which became the plantations. The planters rapidly established themselves in opulence and lived well and gallantly—on slave labor. But, fundamentally, thanks to the soil and the climate which made it flourish, it was tobacco that made this possible.

Because of tobacco, the wife of a successful planter wore silks and satins from Europe instead of rough worsteds such as the Northern farm wife made for herself. Because of tobacco, the Virginia farm family ate delicacies from real china, served in silver utensils, instead of supping on corn meal out of a pine bowl and with a beechen spoon.

True, not all Virginians were wealthy. There were privations for some; and there was a multitude of small farmers. As in Massachusetts, nine tenths of the Virginians were farmers.[1] There was poverty on the frontier, along with hardship and calloused hands. But the great estates, fewer though they were, in their magnificence dwarfed the small holdings.

For example, Doughoregan Manor, the seat of the Carroll family in Maryland, included more than 10,000 acres.[2] For this one dukedom, of course, there were 10,000

small farms of comparatively few acres; but there loomed always the opportunity of attaining riches in a short time. What happened in Virginia was that tobacco created such immediate wealth for every farmer who grew it (and everyone with suitable land did so) that the period of development of the colony from primitive existence to opulent luxury was telescoped into an astonishingly short period of years.

No other agriculture like Virginia's had ever existed before. Cereals always had been the wealth of nations. Never in all history had a commonwealth depended upon a crop which was a luxury and not a food at all.

Tobacco

Tobacco was first made known to the world by Columbus. He mentions it in his diary under date of November 20, 1492.[3] Soon after, it was introduced into Spain; and in 1560 Jean Nicot, Ambassador of France to Portugal, introduced it to Paris, and immortalized himself by giving his name to the plant—*Nicotiana.* By 1586 it had appeared in London, possibly being brought directly from Virginia by Ralph Lane, Raleigh's emissary, who founded the ill-fated colony of Roanoke. It is more likely, however, that English gentlemen, completing their education in Paris, brought the interesting weed home with them before 1586.

By 1600 the use of tobacco had taken a firm hold upon polite Europe. Pope Urban VIII had issued a bull against its use; and King James had issued his famous "Counterblast," saying that smoking was "a custom loathsome to the eye, hateful to the nose, harmful to the brain, dangerous to the lungs, and in the stinking black fume thereof

nearest resembling the horrible Stygian smoke of the pit that is bottomless." [4]

Despite some religious and political opposition, the smoking habit spread like wildfire. Particularly in England, the importation of tobacco became so large that in 1601 Parliament put on tobacco an import duty of six shillings and ten pence a pound. Thus began government revenue on smoking, a method of taxation which has flourished ever since.

Parliament also sold to certain London merchants the exclusive right to manufacture and sell tobacco pipes. [5] This little device brought into the Crown's coffers something like 16,000 pounds annually [6]—a figure which demonstrates how vastly the English were enjoying tobacco.

Thus a tremendous market for tobacco awaited the Virginia farmer. He did not take advantage of it at once. Many early settlers rushed madly through the great forests thinking they would find jewels in the pebbled bottoms of brooks and lumps of pure gold gleaming everywhere. Threatened starvation finally brought them to realize that farming was the only basis upon which the Virginia colony could endure.

The Golden Harvest

The Virginia settler, once turned farmer, was ready for prosperity.

John Rolfe apparently was the first man to experiment with growing the Indian's wild tobacco. [7] Governor Yeardley encouraged the experiments. The farmers turned their cornfields into tobacco patches. For many years the Old Dominion was mastered by tobacco.

The development which followed was magical. First,

tobacco-hungry England was importing some £60,000
(gold specie) worth of tobacco yearly from Spain and
France. Once assured that Virginia could supply the
needs of the nation, Parliament at one stroke cut off the
imports from Spain and France by the simple expedient
of levying prohibitive duties. Thus Virginia was given a
virtual monopoly.[8]

Then, it was soon demonstrated that Virginia alone, of
all the British dominions at the time, could produce tobacco profitably. English and Irish farmers at home hastened to try their luck at cultivating the weed. The damp
climate and higher labor costs proved the attempt futile.
Accordingly, Virginia was left to its opportunity—especially because, to encourage Virginian planters to produce
as much tobacco as possible, Parliament forbade anyone
but Virginians to grow it.

In 1616 conditions were such that Governor Thomas
Dale feared the colony might be pinched for food, because so many farmers devoted all of their land to the
new cash crop. So he ordered each farmer to plant at least
two acres of corn for himself and two for each male servant and member of his family.

Growing a crop of tobacco was not hard work, compared to the raising of corn or wheat. Captain John
Smith[9] said that a farmer could obtain six times as much
for his labor in growing tobacco as in raising wheat.

The Virginia farmer was even more fortunate in the
matter of soil and geographical surroundings. Tobacco
needs not so much a warm and humid climate, which Virginia had, but a deep, rich soil—which Virginia also had.
A thin soil, such as most of New England's, even if the
summers were sometimes warm enough, would not pro-

EARLY TRANSPORTATION
Rolling tobacco from plantation to tidewater
in colonial Virginia

duce a good tobacco crop. There it would grow only in certain alluvial soils, such as are to be found in the Connecticut Valley. Eventually a superior tobacco for cigars was developed in Connecticut.

Virginia's geography was in her favor. Tobacco had to be shipped overseas. This meant transportation. There were no roads for great carts at first, but Virginia had plenty of rivers and creeks that offered cheap, easy transportation. The leaf, packed in hogsheads, was simply rolled overland by the so-called "tobacco roads," which were not roads at all but narrow ways cleared of trees. Along the navigable streams, wharves were built to load the hogsheads into flatbottom scows, which floated down to water deep enough for ships to berth.

Most of the larger plantations were purposely laid out beside navigable streams. The farmer could build his own wharf; and a ship from England could come right to his very front door.

Slavery

Virginia was fortunate in its solution of the labor problem. In the beginning there was the familiar labor shortage. Indentured servants and even shiploads of intended wives for bachelor planters were brought over. But land was so cheap and white labor so dear that this was but a partial solving of the labor situation.

So Negro slavery was introduced. It was a very wasteful system, but it flourished, thanks to the mild climate and the large returns in tobacco raising. Of course it took time to import and to breed slaves. As late as 1671 there were but 2,000 Negro slaves employed, as against 6,000 white bond servants.[10] Very soon, however, the balance

swung the other way, and save for the small farmer, who cultivated his own few acres, Virginia tobacco growing flourished on slave labor.

The colonial Virginian farmer was rarely harsh with his slaves. They were expensive and difficult to obtain. The widespread evils of slavery developed later, under the economic rule of cotton.

A Single Crop

Thus Virginia, and subsequently portions of Maryland and North and South Carolina, developed because of tobacco. However, even with such a money crop as tobacco, the farmer's course did not run smoothly. The basic trouble was that the whole section was dependent upon that single crop. It was used for money. All goods were priced in terms of tobacco—so many pounds of it for so much silk or corn or books. Wages were paid with it and debts discharged by it. In fact, having only one annual crop, the planter usually ran for twelve months on his credit and then settled his accounts in an hour with his year's harvest, if he had enough, and if the prevailing price was sufficiently high. And that was the eternal trouble. The price fluctuated. The more tobacco raised, the lower the price. Tobacco farmers began to worry, and the worry increased as the years went by.

"I tell you, fellows," a leader argued, "we've got to keep up the price by whatever means we can contrive. There's too much tobacco being raised now."

Another shook his head. "We're living much too expensively," he said. "Tobacco prosperity has bred in us a chronic extravagance. The English merchants have wanted so much tobacco that they've granted us credit

much too liberally, in order to encourage us to plant more and more."

"And that has created a vicious cycle of debt, from which many of us can never clear ourselves," added the first planter. "The more we borrow, the more we plant—and the deeper we go into debt, because the price keeps falling."

For English merchants the situation was splendid. They profited both ways. As selling agents, they collected a commission on the English market. As purchasing agents for the planters (whom they held in chains of debt) they collected commission on all the merchandise they procured to be sent back to Virginia. Goods reaching Virginia were priced at three times their cost in London. Prices for the same articles in New York City would be about half what they would cost in Richmond,[11] but the farmer was forced by pressure of debts to purchase from the English sources.

Overproduction

The basic cause of trouble with tobacco was overproduction and the consequent price fluctuation. Here are illustrative figures:[12] In 1619, Virginia sent ten tons of leaf to London, and the price paid was three shillings the pound. Then 250 tons were shipped in 1629, and the price was three pennies the pound. Later, 27,000 tons were shipped (in 1753), and the price was two pennies the pound.

Virginia farmers resorted to many expedients to improve conditions. They tried price fixing. In 1631, for example, the Virginia Colonial Assembly ruled that no

tobacco traded for English goods could be rated at less than six pennies the pound.[13] Then crop control was tried, as production still flooded the market and made price fixing impossible. In 1639, 1640, and 1641, the total crop was supposed to be limited to 1,200,000 pounds of good quality; and English merchants, for their part, agreed to help by accepting 40 pounds of the new crop in cancellation of 100 pounds of old debt on the previous crops. Officials were appointed to destroy inferior tobacco and to burn excess production, while all tobacco was to be rated at not less than three pennies the pound.[14]

But the Virginia farmers were doomed to failure, because all efforts proved to be of merely temporary value. The situation grew ever worse, as Maryland and the Carolinas joined tobacco production and swelled the volume. Attempts were made at inter-colony price pegging and crop control, but they usually failed dismally.

Naturally, smuggling developed, as mariners from New England short-circuited the London merchants, who were supposedly in control of merchandising. Yankees carried contraband cargoes (which they purchased directly from the planters) to France and Germany and back to Boston as well. Smuggling flourished, because, by cutting out the London profits, both the Virginia planter and the Yankee shipmaster could make handsome profits.

The Virginia Assembly from time to time tried to persuade the farmers to grow other crops. Corn, wheat, and cotton were also being propagandized, and an effort was even made to have the farmers grow mulberry trees and to raise silkworms. Still, tobacco ruled because the profits were generally so good, especially for the modest farmer who cultivated his own few acres and did not ape the lux-

ury of Old England, as the large planters did in their constant struggle against debt.

Evidence of this can be seen in the constantly swelling volume of tobacco production. For example, in 1665, the volume of export of the leaf was 27,750,000 pounds. In 1770, on the eve of the Revolution, the total exported was more than 100,000,000 pounds. The value set that year was 900,000 British pounds.[15]

Princely Hospitality

Despite these production and price troubles, tobacco through the years supported a wealthy social life in Virginia and its neighboring colonies for those families which were successful. The period is famed for the princely hospitality of the planters, which, aside from inherited tastes, arose from the isolation of the large plantations. As much of the year as could possibly be lived in the towns was passed there, in a round of social pleasures. But, being farmers, the planters and their families had to live on their land while the crops were being planted, cultivated, and harvested.

With the average large plantation covering about 5,000 acres,[16] it meant that each family was set off by itself. This bar of distance was intensified by wretched roads. For this reason visits even among neighbors were stays of days and even weeks. The farmers' families relieved their boredom by living with each other, and each plantation prided itself upon its lavish hospitality.

Mansion Homes

As the farmers became wealthy or had sufficient credit, their own pride and the pressures of this highly developed

social life led to their building magnificent "mansion houses." Many of these, especially a little later, were distinguished by an ambitious architecture, however poor the actual construction.

Some of these Virginia farm mansions have become famous—for examples, Stratford, 1729; Rosewell, 1725; Westover, 1730; Gunston Hall, 1755; Mount Airy, 1758.[17]

Because of colonial limitations, most of the mansions left much to be desired, in the opinion of some gentlemen whose tastes had been elevated by foreign travel and by familiarity with the stately homes of England. Thomas Jefferson, writing on the subject of Virginian architecture, declared: "The genius of architecture seems to have shed its maledictions over this land. . . . . The first principles of the art are unknown, and there exists scarcely a model among us sufficiently chaste to give us an idea of them."

In the light of the recent restoration of Williamsburg this would seem severe criticism, but it seems clear that the American farmers' mansions did not always equal their English models.

Most of the farmers employed wood for their homes at first, but bricks were soon employed almost altogether, particularly as the forests vanished. Stone was not commonly used, because the fat soil was comparatively free of ledges and boulders.

The first farmer with his wooden construction established the classic plantation style of the Virginian home. It was a long, narrow house, rectangular in shape, with chimney stacks of brick at either end. Later houses, like the mansion at Mt. Vernon, leaned to the classical style, with great pillars and more or less chaste ornamentation.

Fundamentally however, the farmers' mansion houses were but modifications of the English manor house, particularly internally. Just as the New England farmer made the kitchen the main feature of his home, the Virginia farmer built his home around the Central Hall or Great Room. This spacious room was used for many general purposes.

Opening from this central room were the other living rooms, a library, an office for the master, the drawing-rooms, and a morning room for the ladies. From the Hall a gracefully contrived staircase rose to the second story, which was usually given over to bedrooms. If the farmer were prosperous, these manor houses often contained eighteen or twenty rooms, as did Stratford Hall.

The Great Hall held a long dining table of oak. Ordinarily this table was covered with a rough cloth called "Holland," but on special occasions, lovely damask was spread, and the table was graced with china and silver. Incidentally, forks were unknown in the seventeenth century and but little used during most of the eighteenth. The furniture was largely imported, although much was locally made. The china and silver came over from England and France. Often the Great Hall and most of the rooms were paneled with oak. Tapestries graced the walls and carved oak mantels framed the fireplaces.

London Styles

The agricultural luxury was reflected in the clothing these planters wore. It was nearly all imported, and London fashions, although often months old because of the long voyage across the Atlantic, were closely copied. Rich planters wore coats and breeches of the gayest broadcloth,

embroidered waistcoats, silk stockings, starched ruffles about their necks and around their wrists, and powdered wigs.

As for the lovely ladies: "The wardrobe of Mrs. Sarah Willoughby, of Lower Norfolk, consisted of a red, a blue, and a black silk petticoat, a petticoat of India silk and worsted prunella, a striped linen and calico petticoat, a black silk gown, a scarlet waistcoat with silver lace, a white knit waistcoat, a pair of red paragon bodices, a striped stuff jacket, a worsted prunella mantel, a sky-coloured satin bodice, three fine and three coarse Holland (linen) aprons, seven handkerchiefs, and two hoods." [18]

The Scotch-Irish

This gracious life of the wealthy tobacco farmers is not of course the whole picture of farming in colonial Virginia. There were many small farmers who did grow corn, wheat, flax, and various fruits and vegetables, both for their own tables and for the market which supplied the big manor houses. Back from tidewater the soil was not so ideally adapted to tobacco, and so the farmers there, especially during frontier days, lived through the same primitive conditions as were endured by other American frontier farmers.

Virginia and the Carolinas, too, underwent a particularly great change when, at about the opening of the eighteenth century, the flood of Scotch-Irish immigrants poured into the Shenandoah Valley and settled the western portions of the three colonies. These sturdy folk were accomplished farmers, very well educated by the standards of the time, and their impact upon Virginia politically was considerable. This was so especially in the mid-

EARLY TOBACCO CULTURE
Tobacco raising was laborious and also wasteful,
depleting the soil of its fertility

dle of the century, when about 500,000 of them came to America, some to Pennsylvania and New York, but larger numbers to western Virginia.

Like the Puritans, they were an earnest, religious people. How much they contributed to Virginia's share in the Revolution is another matter, but it is certain that they did transform the professions, business, and farming in Virginia and the Carolinas. They held small farms, they hated slavery, and they were backwoods farmers who created a sound and stable agriculture that went far to balance the Virginian preoccupation with tobacco.

Two Great Virginians

How deeply this Scotch-Irish Presbyterianism affected the agricultural life of Virginia can be shown by the writings of two Virginians who, whatever their greatness in other fields, were first of all farmers.

George Washington is one. At Mt. Vernon he was a gentleman farmer. To the 8,077 acres of his first estate, divided into five farms and woodlands, as well as a fishery, a ferry, and two grist mills,[19] he added other lands from time to time until he owned at one time 69,615 acres in thirty-seven localities, as well as twenty-four city lots and one entire city square.[20] Like other Virginians, he grew tobacco. In 1759 he "made" 34,160 pounds of the leaf and, in 1763 the figure was 89,079 pounds. Thereafter he reduced his tobacco crop and after the Revolution raised none at all.[21]

He reduced tobacco production because he recognized that tobacco impoverished the soil. This was a scientific observation. In fact, George Washington was one of

America's early scientific farmers. He investigated soil conservation and labored for years to interest other farmers in problems of erosion and exhaustion. He constantly experimented with seed selection to improve varieties. He proudly boasted that the flour from his own strain of wheat was the best in America. He corresponded abroad to gain new ideas in farming and imported seeds and plants. Clovers and grasses interested him particularly, and he is said to have grown the first alfalfa in America. Livestock was another special interest, and he, as he himself stated, raised the first mules in America. His flock of sheep was constantly bred to increase wool production. His 600 sheep gave, he asserts, 5¼ pounds more wool on the average than any sheep of his neighbors' flocks.[22]

Washington believed that America could remain free from entangling foreign alliances. He believed this nation could be self-supporting through an intelligent agriculture. He writes of this in one of his letters:[23]

"The more I am acquainted with agricultural affairs, the better I am pleased with them; insomuch, that I can nowhere find so great satisfaction as in these innocent and useful pursuits. In indulging these feelings, I am led to reflect how much more delightful to an undebauched mind is the task of making improvements on the earth, than all the vain glory which can be acquired by ravaging it . . . an employment which is more congenial to the natural disposition of mankind than any other."

Jefferson was an even greater Virginian farmer. He had his feet firmly planted in his native soil. His classical estate, Monticello, was made self-supporting as a farm. Here Jefferson not only made money but also operated an experiment station for new seeds, new plants, new trees,

new farm tools, and even machines. His farmering philosophy he expressed in these words:[24]

"Those who labor in the earth are the chosen people of God . . . It is the focus in which He keeps alive that sacred fire, which might otherwise escape from the face of the earth. Corruption of morals in the mass of cultivators is a phenomenon of which no age or nation has furnished an example. It is the mark set on those who, not looking up to heaven, to their own toil and industry, as does the husbandman, for their subsistence, depend for it on the casualties and caprice of customers. Dependence begets subservience and venality, suffocates the germ of virtue, and prepares fit tools for the designs of ambition . . . generally speaking, the proportion which the aggregate of the other classes of citizens bears in any State to that of its husbandmen, is the proportion of its unsound to its healthy parts, and is a good enough barometer whereby to measure its degree of corruption . . ."

Again, in a letter to John Jay, Jefferson declared:[25]

". . . Cultivators of the earth are the most valuable citizens. They are the most vigorous, the most independent, the most virtuous, and they are tied to their country, and wedded to its liberty and interests, by the most lasting bonds . . ."

[1,2] Andrews, Charles M. *Colonial Folkways*. New Haven. 1919

[3] Fiske, John. *Old Virginia and Her Neighbors*. Boston. 1897

[4] *Black's History of England*. London. 1870 (No author given)

[5] Jacobstein. *The Great Colonial Staple. Columbia University Studies in History, Economics and Public Law*. Vol. 26. No. 3. New York. 1907

[6,7,8] Jacobstein. *Op. cit.*

[9] Smith, John. *History of Virginia*. Various reprints.

[10,12] Jacobstein. *Op. cit.*

[11] McMaster, John B. *History of the People of the United States*. New York. 1913

[13] Edwards, Everett E. *U. S. Dept. of Agri. Year Book*. 1940

[14] Gray, L. C. *History of Agriculture in the Southern United States.* Carnegie Inst. Wash. 1933

[15] Edward, Everett E. *Op. cit.*

[16] Page, Thomas Nelson. *The Old Dominion,* etc. New York. 1908

[17] Wilstach, Paul. *Tidewater Virginia.* Indianapolis. 1929

[18] Bruce, Phillip A. *Economic History of Virginia,* etc. New York. 1895

[19, 20, 21, 22] Edwards, Everett E. *Washington Bureau of Agricultural Economics. U. S. Dept. of Agri.* Washington. 1937

[23] Knight, Franklin, Ed. *George Washington.* Washington, D. C. 1847

[24] Jefferson, Thomas. *Notes on Virginia.* 1785

[25] Washington, H. A., Ed. *Writings of Thomas Jefferson.* Washington, D. C. 1853

CHAPTER VIII

THE SOUTH—RICE, INDIGO, AND SILK

LET us view the possessions of William Dry, planter on the Cooper River, South Carolina:

". . . a good brick dwelling house, two brick store houses, a brick kitchen and wash-house, a brick necessary house, a barn with a large brick chimney, several rice mills, motars, etc., a winnowing house, an oven, a large stable and coach house, a cooper's shop, a house built for a smith's shop; a garden on each side of the house . . . a fish pond, well stored with perch, roach, pike, eels, and catfish . . . an orchard of very good apple and peach trees, a corn house and poultry house . . . and at least 400 acres of land, all cleared . . . the whole having a clay foundation and not deep; the great part of it fenced in . . ."[1]

If we visited with the Dry family in winter, we would find them at home in Charleston, where their town house would offer lavish hospitality. We would enjoy gay balls, dinner parties, and evenings at the theatre. We might realize that most of colonial America was still struggling with the primitive poverties of wilderness life, but with the Drys in Charleston we almost could fancy ourselves in London. Back on their plantation in summer, we would be with farmers, but still every luxury of the time would be at our command.

South Carolina farmers developed for themselves a life which, for the fortunate, was glamorous and romantic. Indeed, the colony began with the deliberate establishment of an aristocracy based upon the ownership of land.[2]

A planter holding 48,000 acres or more became a landgrave; one with 24,000 acres was named a cacique; and one with 12,000, a baron. Most Carolina settlers found these titles absurd, and they soon were forgotten. One reason for the collapse of the system was that very few planters managed to gather and to hold more than a few thousand acres. The larger plantations seldom ran to more than 5,000 acres,[3] and farms a tenth that size were the usual establishments. No doubt the aristocratic beginning influenced the social life of the colony,[4] and many prominent aristocrats appeared in the course of time—men like Landgrave Thomas Smith, who served as Governor of Carolina in 1695.

The colony enjoyed agricultural prosperity almost from the very beginning because of two special crops, rice and indigo. In the cultivation of these two products the colony came to enjoy a virtual monopoly. What tobacco was to Virginia, rice and indigo were to the future State of South Carolina.

North Carolina

What is now North Carolina did not have such a fortunate history as its sister commonwealth. North Carolina was poverty-stricken and submerged in constant difficulties for many years.

South Carolina had the advantage of having its own great port of Charleston to link it with London and the rest of the world. North Carolina had no port at all and

was forced to trade through Norfolk, Virginia. Everything coming into North Carolina and everything going out was filtered through the hands of the merchants of Norfolk. Furthermore, North Carolina remained a frontier area for many years because of the particularly vigorous and belligerent Indian tribes which inhabited most of the section.

Another factor kept North Carolina in the background. This section was the "backwoods" of both Virginia and South Carolina and a natural haven for criminals and escaped bondservants. The settlers thus came to have the reputation of being lawless men—fugitives or renegades who thwarted all constituted order and delighted in refusing to pay taxes. Then also, the lands along the North Carolina coast, which would otherwise have been preferable because they were linked with the other colonies and the Old World by the sea, were swampy and poorly suited for farming. For all these reasons, North Carolina did not at first largely attract ambitious farmers and men with means.

Criticism of North Carolina abounds in colonial literature. In 1729 Colonel Byrd wrote of Edenton, then the seat of the nominal government:[5] "I believe this is the only metropolis in the Christian or Mohammedan world where there is neither church, chapel, mosque, synagogue, or any other place of worship of a sect or religion whatsoever."

"Hillbilly" sloth may here have had its beginnings. Of the farmers of North Carolina, the Colonel wrote:[6] ". . . they pay no tribute, either to God or to Caesar. . . . They make their wives rise out of their beds early in the morning, and at the same time that they lie and snore till

the sun has run one third of his course and dispersed all the unwholesome damps. Then after stretching and yawning for full half an hour, they light their pipes, and under the protection of a cloud of smoke, venture out into the open air . . . they stand leaning with both their arms upon the cornfield fence, and gravely consider whether they had best go and take a small heat at the hoe, but generally find reasons to put it off until another time. Thus they loiter away their lives, like Solomon's sluggard, and at the winding up of the year scarcely have bread to eat."

North Carolina had to develop eventually, however, for it is one of the forty-eight States most fortunate in natural resources. Many of these first settlers or their descendants were edged westward into the mountains. Here some remain to this day, and are sometimes but not always justly called "poor whites."

The new development for North Carolina came at about 1720, when a tide of settlers, mostly Scotch-Irish, flowed down the mountain valleys from Pennsylvania and Virginia. There were also settlers of French Huguenot, Dutch, German, Swiss, and Irish stock. These were all hardy, thrifty, ambitious, and energetic people. These solid farmers were the saving grace of North Carolina. By 1750 the "bad days" of the preceding century were a thing forgotten except in the remote hills.

Unlike South Carolina, North Carolina did not boast a great staple crop. Agriculture was diversified, and for many years most of the farms were operated on a self-sufficient basis. Tobacco was grown, but as it was shipped out via Virginia, profits were not large for the planter of North Carolina. The farmers in the Cape Fear region grew some rice, and all the farmers in the forested sections

produced tar, turpentine, and yellow pine timber. Some of the settlers along shore were fishermen, but piracy flourished there with the aid of the settlers, and the fisheries did not amount to much.

"Black Cattle"

By 1729, however, when the city of Brunswick was laid out, and the Crown took over the colony, larger plantations were founded. Soon Wilmington grew into a thriving center, which ended the colony's isolation. Corn and other staple crops began to be marketed. The excellence of Carolina corn, for example, became celebrated in the London export trade. More important, North Carolina began to export its famous "black cattle." The name was a colloquial term used at the time to designate beef cattle of any color.

Ranching in America probably began with these herds, at a date about 1680. At that time North Carolina was practically all one unfenced pasture, and the cattle were allowed to run wild. By 1730 the cattle were so numerous and profits from them so attractive that many farmers fenced in their lands and gave some attention to breeding. An anonymous author[7] declared that herds numbering 2000 were owned by individuals, and that "such herds of cattle and swine are to be found in no other colony." According to other writers these "black cattle" were marketed by being driven overland to cities such as Charleston, Norfolk, Baltimore, and Philadelphia.

Swine, allowed to run wild in the forests, reverted to almost a wild state. Known as "razorbacks" because of their leanness, they supplied excellently flavored hams

and bacon; and thus "Virginia" ham gained a reputation which has long endured.

North Carolina farmers were not successful with sheep, because wolves killed them; but goats could defend themselves and accordingly flourished. Horse breeding was not important at first, but soon after 1700 the farmers turned to breeding superior stock. Soon the future State was a thriving center for horses, and particularly for riding horses.

Rice

In sharp contrast to this diversity in North Carolina, the planter in South Carolina enjoyed early prosperity with his two staple crops of rice and indigo.

Rice was the more important of the two. The farmer probably was planting it as early as 1669.[8] The rice, however, was a dry-soil variety grown in the upland soils and was not of much importance as an exportable staple.

Then, in 1694, according to the story,[9] a British ship sailing home from Madagascar was so battered by a storm that it put into Charleston to refit. The Captain had a small bag of unhulled East Indian rice, a wet-soil variety, which he presented to a family that had entertained him.

Members of this family, having once lived in the East Indies, were familiar with rice culture there. They planted their gift of rice in the neighboring marshlands, and the rice prospered amazingly. If the story is true, this was the beginning of Carolina's rice growing. The variety of rice which was grown in Carolina, known as "Carolina white," is now standard the world over and is grown everywhere. It remains the trade's highest type of excel-

lence, although Carolina itself is no longer an important producer.

Against this story, there are records that in 1677 the proprietors of the South Carolina colony were active in London in attempting to find new varieties of rice seed with which to experiment in Carolina. Many years were occupied by South Carolina planters in fixing upon the best variety for their particular climate and soil.

At any event, rice culture began to prosper amazingly in the lush lowlands. They were originally salt marshes, but the planters reclaimed them by throwing up dykes, which kept out the salt water and impounded the fresh water flowing through the area in a multitude of streams. By cleverly contrived gates in the dykes, the water level over the fields was controlled at will.

The method proved ideal. By 1740 the annual production of rice was about 200,000 pounds.[10] Charleston exported 100,000 barrels in 1753; and 125,000 barrels were sent out in 1775.[11]

Slaves

There was a fatal flaw, however, in this popular rice production.

"I'm giving it up," grumbled a rice grower to a visitor. "Rice is a crop that requires a powerful lot of cheap hand labor. You've not only got to have a number of hands— you've got to drive them hard. And you have to buy the very cheapest slaves in order to keep the investment as low as possible."

"I thought native-born slaves were all high-priced," remarked the visitor.

"So they are," replied the planter. "To get cheap ones,

you have to buy Negroes straight from Africa. And
they're bewildered, stubborn, and bitter. Not much good
for any continuous labor."

Naturally, with such material, stern methods were required. Because the farmers themselves seldom managed
their slaves directly but left the work to overseers—whose
quality can be imagined by their accepting such employment—brutality was sometimes practiced.[12] Occasionally,
sections of the South Carolina rice plantation area were in
fear of a slave uprising. Farmers carried arms as a habit.[13]
Such a rebellion might have been a dreadful experience,
for in 1760, of the 200,000 inhabitants of South Carolina,
150,000 were Negroes.[14]

There was actually one such rebellion in 1740. Cato, a
slave on a plantation near Stone Inlet, gathered a horde
of his fellows and killed several white families—men,
women, and children. The farmers reacted promptly. A
large posse rounded up the rebels, slaughtered most of
them in a sharp attack, and then hanged to the nearest
trees all that remained of the suspected leaders.[15]

The ultimate end of slave labor spelled the ruin of the
rice plantations. Rice culture moved into the Mississippi
delta and, going on to Arkansas and California, is now
flourishing, thanks to the machines that have replaced
arduous hand labor.

A woman[16] who tried her hand at rice planting, having
in her youth managed a Carolina rice farm, closed her
autobiography with these words: "The rice planting
which for years gave me the exhilaration of making a
good income for myself, is a thing of the past—the banks
and trunks (dykes and gates) have been washed away,
and there is no money to replace them."

Indigo

As for indigo, which the farmer planted only for a comparatively brief period, it was a staple which for colonial farms yielded a high return. The colony's proprietors instructed the farmers in South Carolina as early as 1690 to grow the plant, and in 1694 Parliament passed acts to encourage the development of the crop.[17] However, these early attempts failed, for it was not until 1740 that indigo production was established sufficiently to lead the farmers to risk sizeable plantings.

Before the days of coal tar dyes, indigo was one of the world's great dye plants. It was an oriental staple, and Europe imported so much of it that British authorities sought during the seventeenth century to establish indigo plantations within the Empire. About 1700, such plantations were started on the West Indian island of Antigua; and there were efforts to do likewise on a serious scale in South Carolina.

According to local legend, a young lady made indigo planting possible. The Governor of Antigua, Sir George Lucas, sent some seeds of the indigo plant to his daughter, Miss Elizabeth, who was visiting in Charleston.[18] She planted the seeds, raised a crop and experimented with technical methods of extracting the dye. Somehow she hit upon an expert fermentation system and produced a dye of superior quality.

Parliament was forthwith informed and received samples; and the astute legislators reacted by granting a bounty on all Carolina-produced indigo. From that day on until the Revolution, indigo culture flourished wondrously. About 216,924 pounds[19] were exported in 1754, and 1,130,662[20] pounds were sent to England in 1775.

To summarize: South Carolina and to a much lesser extent, Georgia, flourished with the two staples of rice and indigo. Rice culture endured as long as slavery made it possible. Indigo faded from the picture after the American Revolution, because the British bounty ended with Britain's loss of the colonies. During this colonial period, cotton was not important, although by the time of the Revolution, South Carolina alone was producing a million pounds.

Silk

Silk was produced in the Carolinas and in Georgia, as well as in other colonies, but it remained more of a cherished dream than a reality. Miss Lucas, of indigo fame, pioneered also in silk culture. She actually grew enough silk to make herself three gowns.

The interest in silk culture began when the colonists discovered the mulberry tree native in Virginia, the Carolinas, and Georgia. This is the food plant of the silkworm. What, asked the farmer, would be simpler than to import the worms and produce silk? Parliament thought the idea wonderful, for Italy was taking millions of pounds of gold from England every year in return for the silk its merchants imported from the Orient.

Virginia in 1619 ordered each man to plant six mulberry trees annually for seven years. Later, Virginia brought over Armenian silk experts to initiate the industry; and, when interest flagged, in 1656 a bonus of 4,000 pounds of tobacco was given to one of these experts to stimulate his efforts.[21] Such attempts, including Government bounties, had some effect; and 300 pounds of raw

silk, as an example of the production built up, were sent back to England in 1730.

South Carolina experimented officially much as did Virginia, but results were disappointing. Georgia, however, went into the business seriously. Every farmer was required to plant mulberry trees in order to obtain and hold land and, at government expense, programs of education and propaganda were carried along vigorously. The colony even built a factory for reeling the silk from the cocoons spun by the worms.

By this artificial stimulation, Georgia did produce silk —as much as 1,084 pounds in 1766, the leading year.[22] Production thereafter sharply declined. Silk production failed to interest the farmer, because the vast amount of hand labor involved was too great and too costly to make the crop profitable.

The farmers of Georgia experimented with grapes, limes, oranges, and lemons; but in the main, it was rice and indigo, corn and flax, cattle and pigs, and timber and naval stores that this southernmost colony produced.

Spanish America

In Florida and in the lower Mississippi region, as well as in New Mexico and California, the Spanish settlers in what was to become part of the United States succeeded in establishing an Arcadian agriculture. The Spanish farmer copied his ancestral farm in Old Spain as nearly as local conditions would allow. The estates, particularly in California, were vast. Money was of little value; but food, clothing, and all the real necessaries of life were abundant. It was a feudal system, with the farmer the lord

of all the land he cared to claim. His children formed an aristocracy. The Indians formed the peasantry.

The fragment of Florida that was under cultivation produced abundantly of fruits and crops, such as sugar cane and oranges. Life flowed in leisurely fashion there, to judge by the old houses still standing in St. Augustine. In the Mississippi delta, sugar cane was being raised, and such crops as figs thrived well. Everywhere, cattle and horses prospered.

In the Spanish Far West, aridity made irrigation necessary for corn, grapes, wheat, beans, pumpkins, peppers, figs, oranges, lemons, limes, and all the rest. But there was Indian labor to build the dams and the ditches to make the desert flower, and agriculture prospered through the years—until the United States took over each Spanish section in its turn.

An Independent America

Thus American agriculture progressed during the hundred and fifty years from the first settlements to the Revolution. The American colonist, turned farmer through necessity and by inclination, accomplished a miracle fully as great as his descendants have done since 1776.

The farmers had cleared away the forest only in a narrow band along the Atlantic coast, a mere sliver of space compared to what lay over the mysterious mountain wall. But by being successful cultivators of the soil, the thirteen colonies were economically independent. In the beginning, they were tied to England's apron strings and were, to a degree, helpless socially, economically, and physically. By 1776 the colonies were strong enough to stand on their own feet and win their independence.

That was the great job accomplished by the colonial farmer. He established America.

[1, 2, 3] Andrews, Charles M. *Colonial Folkways.* New Haven. 1919
[4] Fiske, John. *Old Virginia and Her Neighbors.* Boston. 1897
[5, 6] Byrd MSS: 1,59. Quoted by Fiske, *Op. cit.*
[7] Anonymous (Possibly Dr. John Mitchell). *American Husbandry.* London. 1775
[8] Bogart, E. L. *Economic History of the American People.* New York. 1935
[9] Copeland, Edwin B., *Rice.* London. 1924
[10] Fiske, John. *Op. cit.*
[11] Bogart, E. L. *Op. cit.*
[12] de Crevecoeur, St. John. *Letters.* Philadelphia. 1793
[13, 14, 15] John Fiske, *Old Virginia,* etc. Boston. 1897
[16] Pennington, Patience. *A Woman Rice Planter.* New York. 1913
[17] Edwards, Everett E. *Yearbook. Op. cit.*
[18, 19] Bailey, L. H. *Cyclopedia of American Agriculture.* New York. 1911
[20] Faulkner, Harold U. *American Economic History.* New York. 1925
[21, 22] Edwards, Everett E. *Op. cit.*

PART III
THE GREAT EXPANSION, 1784-1861

CHAPTER IX

KING COTTON

AFTER the Revolution established the United States, and subsequent political and social circumstances opened the continent to our stupendous national expansion, the Southern farmer was the most fortunate agriculturist in history.

Until the Civil War brought ruin and depression to the South, many a farmer was carried headlong on a tide of prosperity. As a result, the fabulous ante-bellum period wrote into our national experience one of the most romantic and glamorous chapters of our boisterous annals.

Here is the situation: The Northern States, while always agricultural in the sense that farming continued to be the way of life for multitudes of families, turned more and more from the soil to other activities. Chief of these were foreign trade and industry. The old folks might remain on the farm, but most of the children flocked to the cities and towns to work in the mills, the factories, the stores, and the counting-rooms. The more adventurous boys went to sea, and, roaming the world, made the Stars and Stripes familiar in every port where a dollar could be turned.

But the South remained largely agricultural. The farmer continued to grow tobacco. Rice and indigo had become unprofitable, and even tobacco was no longer so much of a money crop as formerly. Foreign production

of tobacco was competing in the British markets with the American leaf. A more serious fact was that the careless farmer had so exhausted his soils that the return for his labor was considerably shrunken. New soils were the answer, so, although the old tobacco States of Virginia and the Carolinas continued to produce tobacco, many farmers found it cheaper to move to new soil than to struggle with the old farm. Thus Kentucky became a tobacco State, and so did Ohio, Tennessee, and Missouri. Louisville and St. Louis in time became important tobacco markets.

The farmer in Carolina still grew rice; but the crop was similarly slipping from his hands because of high labor costs and because rice growing was becoming established in the Mississippi delta area. Actually, the rice farmers of the Atlantic marshes had their best year in 1850; but it was a hollow triumph, for the costs of slaves had risen to such heights (as much as $2000 for an ordinary field hand) that the rice farmer was really losing money. After 1850, rice farming in the old South steadily declined, and Mississippi, Louisiana, and Alabama took it over.

The farmer in Virginia, with his fields now too poor for tobacco, could turn to raising flax and hemp. Flax became important and was shipped in great quantities to Northern linen mills. But Kentucky and Tennessee, with their richer soils, took the lead in hemp production, and it seemed for a time that America was developing another important staple crop. However, Russian hemp came into the market and undersold the native fibre—and that ended hemp as a big crop for the American farmer.

There were other activities which the farmer in the

South could follow profitably. For example, the South in ante-bellum days grew not merely 80 per cent of America's tobacco, but some 50 per cent of the corn, 70 per cent of the peas and beans, 94 per cent of the sweet potatoes, and about 30 per cent of the wheat.[1] Then, too, the South was famous for its livestock. Kentucky bluegrass bred the best of horses, horned cattle, and hogs, while Virginia led in sheep.

This is only the general picture of what the ordinary farmer busied himself to produce. There still remained the two great crops of the South.

Sugar Cane

The first of these was sugar. From an insignificant beginning just before the Revolution, by the time of the Civil War the sugar cane plantations, mostly centered in southeastern Louisiana, had grown to a major position in American agriculture. In 1823 some 20,000 tons of sugar were marketed; in 1861 the figure was 270,000 tons.[2] Sugar cane was probably introduced into Louisiana by Jesuit priests from Santo Domingo about 1751. For many years the culture was of no importance. It was not until about 1800 that farmers in that almost frost-free region realized how fortunate they were.[3]

The good news spread through the South; and many farmers who possessed the necessary capital moved to Louisiana. The migration was particularly marked from South Carolina, where rice culture was becoming threadbare. This resulted in a draining of slaves away from the rice plantations; it also resulted in a rise in the value of Negro chattels, thus still further reducing the net income of the rice farmers by adding to their overhead.

Cotton

The second great crop of the South was cotton. Of all the farms in the United States today, one third of them, or around 2,100,000,[4] are officially classified as cotton producers. An agricultural map of America shows the cotton belt running east and west for 1,600 miles, from the Carolinas to Oklahoma and from Tennessee down into Texas, the width varying from 150 to 500 miles. These cotton farms occupy about 295,000,000[5] acres. The value of the cotton grown is now about a quarter of all American farm products.[6]

To the Southern farmers, cotton was even more important before "The War." For them, cotton was King. Not only did it provide most of the South's income, but it dominated politics and all social and economic activities.

Cotton was important in the North, as well. Cotton mills were a major industrial activity, especially in New England. Old England, too, was avid for Southern cotton. In fact, the political leaders of the South finally became convinced that the British textile mills needed cotton so badly that England would support the South in its attempts at secession.

Ante-Bellum Romance

Upon cotton the Southern farmer developed a glamorous culture. The golden stream of income supported for years a gay and carefree life, a period embellished by graceful women and polished gentlemen. There was an atmosphere of calm, poise, and dignity about the white houses set amid gracious gardens and wide lawns. Hospitality, always a Southern tradition, was carried to ex-

EARLY COTTON GIN IN CAROLINA

treme lengths; and the tables of the planters were graced by the elegancies of great wealth.

The plantation farmer who flourished under King Cotton's rule was not a citizen of such a humdrum thing as a farming kingdom. The crass details of raising cotton, no less than the dusty matter of commerce and marketing, was left by the planters to their overseers, their business agents, and the "mercenary North." Planters merely ordered their cotton planted, cultivated, harvested, and pressed into bales by their slaves, later to be delivered to market towns, such as those which sprang up along the broad artery of the Mississippi and its lesser tributaries. There, the direct interest of the owners ended. Hired help and slaves did the rest.

Gold flowed back to them in what seemed a perpetual stream. Should they need more money than they had, next year's crop could always be mortgaged.

"We just don't raise anything but cotton," many of the planters asserted.

"Why not?" the newcomer would ask.

And the answer was always the same: "Because we get more money from cotton than we could from all the other crops put together."

"But what about things you need on the plantation—things to eat and wear?"

"We buy corn and salt fish in the markets to feed our slaves; and hemp and coarse cotton to clothe them. It's much cheaper than producing them ourselves," was again the inevitable explanation.

Similarly, these citizens neglected industry—although among them were voices crying in the wilderness. Farseeing Southerners foresaw trouble. They pleaded for

local mills, so that the South could spin its own cotton and gain the profits the North was reaping. These gentlemen watched with uneasiness the spinning westward of the web of Northern railroads and the constant development of Northern ports, draining all the produce of the West. The South did try to send its own railroads also to the West. But cotton was King! His subjects were lavishly rewarded. So, most farmers concluded, why bother disturbing things as they richly and plentifully were?

The Rift in the Lute

Of course, it is not true, romantic novelists to the contrary, that all cotton planters enjoyed luxury.[7] Southern farms were well divided into small, medium, and large holdings. Probably seventy-five per cent of them were small; most of them so small that they did not require slave labor. Actually, in 1860, of the 793,493 families in the South, only 348,000 families owned slaves. Of the slaveholders, only two per cent owned more than fifty slaves. Yet this two per cent, since they were the wealthy families, largely controlled the political and social activities of the time.[8]

These families supplied the South with such leaders as Pinckney, Tyler, Polk, Claiborne, and many others. In fact, plantation farmers of the wealthy type were very much in the minority, but they received most of the publicity. Instead, it was the yeoman farmer who really typified the South. His is the type that should have been publicized. Of course it was cotton and the development of the crop that caused this gathering up of wealth and influence for such a few families.

Cotton is one of the most ancient of crops. It dates back

at least 5,000 years into Egypt. In America, the first farmers in the South, where the climate was suitable, grew it from earliest colonial days. The farmer had a green-seeded, short-stapled variety from which it was a very tedious and laborious task to separate the clinging fibres from the seed.

In 1786 the famous sea-island variety with its long fibres and its easily removed seeds was introduced. However, it was merely locally important, because it would thrive only on the lowlands along the southeast coast. Thus there was too little land available for any major development of sea-island cotton.

Then, about 1800, three things climaxed to put King Cotton on the throne.

Cotton Spinning and Weaving

The first of these was the revolution of cotton textile manufacture in England. Between 1767 and 1780, Hargreave, Crompton, and Arkwright, to name but three inventors, constructed their spinning machines. These, with the application of steam and water power, established concentrations of production. Cotton manufacture was taken out of the cottages and made into a factory industry.

To this spinning improvement, in 1785 were added the weaving machines of Cartwright and others. The result, especially as it was a part of the industrial revolution, caused a tremendous increase in the making of cotton cloth, a vast expansion of the market because of lowered prices, and the establishment of a still more avid market for raw cotton.

New England joined the parade. Such cities of Massachusetts as Lowell, Lawrence, Haverhill, and New Bed-

ford hummed with mills. In New England in 1807 there were but fifteen cotton mills with some 8,000 spindles. In 1811, only four years later, there were eighty-seven mills and 500,000 spindles. Some 76,000 men, women, and children found employment in them.[9]

The Cotton Gin

The second development was the invention of the cotton gin in 1793 by Eli Whitney. His story is a classic familiar to every American.

What the gin accomplished, even in its first crude form, was to make it possible for a slave turning a crank to clean about fifty pounds of the green-seed, short-staple cotton a day. With power the same machine could clean a thousand pounds a day.

The original gin was merely a cylinder set with teeth that protruded through strips of metal. These strips picked up the cotton and drew it through the revolving teeth. The teeth held fast to the fibres, while the seeds dropped out. A second cylinder, set with brushes, met the first cylinder and picked the fibres from the teeth.

Eli Whitney

In his own words, this is how Eli Whitney came to invent the cotton gin:[10]

"I went from New York with the family of the late Major General Greene to Carolina . . . to their plantation about twelve miles from Savannah . . . During this time I heard much said of the extreme difficulty of ginning cotton, that is, separating it from its seeds. There were a number of very respectable gentlemen at Mrs. Greene's who all agreed that if a machine could be in-

vented which would gin cotton with expedition, it would be a great thing both to the Country and the inventor. I involuntarily happened to be thinking on the subject and struck out a plan of a Machine in my mind which I communicated to Miller (who is agent to the executors of General Greene and resides in the family, a man of respectability and property).

"He was pleased with the plan and said if I would pursue it and try an experiment to see if it would answer, he would bear the whole expense. I should lose nothing but my time and if I succeeded we would share in the profits . . . In about ten days, I made a little model for which I was offered, if I would give up all right and title to it, a Hundred Guineas (about $500). I turned my attention to perfecting the machine. I made one before I came away which required the labor of one man to turn it and with which one man will clean ten times as much cotton as he can in any other way before known, and also cleanse it much better than in the usual mode. . . . ."

Successful so far, Whitney and Miller then made their big mistake. Instead of selling manufacturing rights, they began to manufacture the machines themselves. They actually could produce less than a thousandth of the machines the planters desired. More than a hundred individuals and companies responded by manufacturing gins, and Whitney and Miller went to law to defend their rights. They failed dismally—for the Solid South arrayed itself against them.

Whitney's cotton gin proved the key that opened the door to cotton culture. The short-stapled variety could now be produced profitably; and since it could be grown almost anywhere, things really began to hum.

Slavery

The third development which made the reign of King Cotton possible was the extension of slavery. Sentiment against slavery was growing through the South after the Revolution, and slavery probably would have died a natural death after a time. For example, George Washington wrote to a friend in 1794:[11]

"Were it not that I am principled against selling Negroes as you would cattle in a market I would not in 12 months be possessed of a single one as a slave. I shall be happily mistaken if they are not found to be a very troublesome species of property ere many years have passed over our heads."

But cotton culture radically changed the development of this humane idea. Cotton is an easy crop to grow. It is perfectly suited to unskilled labor. It employs labor of all ages, from stalwart men and patient women to small children. Then, too, it is, or was then, almost a year-round business. Planted in the spring, cultivated in the summer, harvested in the fall, it was ginned and baled during the winter. Only a very little direction was needed. The white planter or his overseer told the slaves what to do, how and when to do it, and saw to it that they did it.

The extent of the employment of slaves is shown by various figures. Between 1803 and 1808, when the United States prohibited their importation, South Carolina alone brought in 39,000 slaves. In 1800, when the cotton gin became general in use, there were about a million slaves in the United States. By 1860 the total number of slaves was 4,441,000.[12]

Similarly, the price of slaves rose. About 1776 a slave in good condition was worth about $300. In 1830 a slave

was worth $800; and in 1860 his price had risen to $2,000.[13] Of the 12,000,000 inhabitants of the fifteen so-called slave States in 1860, about one third were slaves.[14]

It was a vicious economic circle and one with profound national significance. The more cotton grown, the more slaves needed; the more slaves, the more land required. And so came about the struggle for new slave States in the Union—one of the causes of friction that led eventually to the Civil War.

With cotton thus enthroned upon slave labor, with mills hungry for the fibres all over the world, and with the cotton gin making production profitable, cotton production increased mightily. Here are a few comparative figures: There were 73,222 bales of cotton marketed in 1800; in 1840, the amount was 1,347,640 bales; in 1860 it was 3,841,416 bales.[15]

Despite the magnificent life King Cotton furnished for many, cotton as the chief crop of the South was not without its troubles.

More and More Land

First, cotton was a crop which demanded not only land but capital to be invested in slaves. Hence, as usually happens, a conflict developed between the small farmer and the large plantation owner. It was another one of the struggles between individualism and capitalism.

Basically, what happened was simple. The cotton planter, caught in the trap of his need for ever-expanding production, had to have more and more land. Unless he cared to move westward, all he could do was to buy up the acres of the smaller farmers about him. So the small farmer sold out, not being able to resist the bait of a good

price for his land. Then, he himself either went westward, where with his money he could re-establish himself more largely, or else he moved onto sub-marginal land near his old home—and watched his fortunes and his family gradually run downhill.

Here is an eye-witness account of the process: "The cotton growing portion of the valley of the Mississippi, the very garden of the Union, is year by year being wrested from the hands of the small farmer and delivered over to the great capitalists . . . All the great cotton lands were first opened by industrious settlers, with small means and much energy. No sooner is their clearing made, and their homestead growing in comfort, than the great planter comes up from the East, with his black horde, settles down on the district, and absorbs and overruns everything. This is precisely the process which is going on, day by day, over the greater portion of Louisiana and Mississippi. The small farmers, that is to say, the mass of the population, are fast disappearing. The rich bottom lands of that glorious valley are being concentrated in the hands of the large planters with from one hundred to one thousand negroes . . ." [16]

However, the life of the big planters was not all honey and wine. Few of them managed to accumulate any surplus. The customary luxurious life consumed practically all of the income. Plantation life was like a land boom. It was economically unsound, and it withered at the first blight of adversity, leaving ruin everywhere.

It was estimated that a slave produced only half as much as a free man would.[17] It is clear that slaves did not pay enough to make them a sound investment. As another writer expressed it, "The economic defects of slave labor

may be summed up under the three following heads: it is given reluctantly, it is unskillful, it is wanting in versatility." [18]

Thus the Southern planter labored under a fatal handicap. Only as long as his market remained good was he safe. A smaller investment in other forms of agriculture, provided they were diversified enough, would have given the South a much sounder even if less glamorous life.

Of course the flames of the Civil War blasted King Cotton from his throne; and in the general ruin, all types of Southern agriculture lay prostrate until society was reconstructed, painfully and slowly. However, it is only fair to say that the pre-occupation of the ante-bellum South with cotton intensified its collapse and lengthened its period of prostration.

[1,2] Edwards, Everett E. *Op. cit.*

[3] Brandes, E. E. X. et. al. *Sugar. U. S. Dept. of Agri. Yearbook.* 1923

[4,5,6] Baker, O. E. *Agricultural Regions of the U. S. U. S. Dept. of Agri.* 1925.

[7] Owsley, Frank and Harriet. *Economic Basis of Society in the Late Ante-Bellum South.* Journal of Southern History, 6:24-25. 1940

[8] Buck, Paul H. *The Poor Whites of the Ante-Bellum South.* Am. Hist. Rev. 1925

[9] Beard, Charles and Mary. *Basic History of the United States.* 1944

[10] Whitney, Eli. *Correspondence. American Historical Review.* III, 99-101

[11] Mazyck, Walter H. *George Washington and the Negro.* Washington. 1932

[12] Seventh United States Census.

[13] Dodd, W. I. *The South in the Building of the Nation.* Vol. 5. pp. 359

[14] Cairnes, John E. *The Slave Power.* 2nd Ed. London. 1863

[15] *United States Department of Agriculture. Reports.*

[16,17] Olmstead, Frederick. *A Journey Into the Back Country.* New York. 1860

[18] Cairnes. *Op. cit.*

CHAPTER X

"BUSTING THE PRAIRIE SOD"

SETTLERS in America came to know that continental America was a great bowl. Forested mountains rimmed the East and the West. Between lay the great grasslands —the prairies and the Great Plains. For millenniums of years the prairies had been covered with grass. When the first settlers roamed over it, the matted roots formed a sod so deep, so heavy, so strong that it mocked the efforts of an ordinary plow.

"The prairie grass simply can't be rooted out nor burned out," the settlers told one another. "This land can never be made ready for planting. It is fit only for the herding of cattle."

"Any land can be farmed," was the stubborn rejoinder of another type of settler, "by good hard work."

These conflicting views—of the rancher and of the farmer—were the basis of a long period of competition in which, for a time, the farmers overwhelmingly won.

Transformation

In 1790, when the Revolution ended, Middle America was empty of colonists. But by the time the Civil War began, that prairie sod had been "busted open," and the nation had become a prosperous agricultural empire 3,000 miles wide. The spectacle of this transformation of the

vast wilds is one of the mightiest dramas of history. That tremendous migration had taken place within the span of a human lifetime, from 1790 to 1860—in seventy years.[1]

Two sets of figures tell the story. In 1790 there were about 4,000,000 persons in the United States. Of these, 94 per cent were settled in the original thirteen States. Only a handful of hardy souls had crossed the grim mountain wall.[2] By 1850 there were 23,000,000 persons in the United States.[3] The frontier had leaped over the Appalachians, forded the Mississippi, paused briefly in Minnesota, Iowa, and Texas; and then, hopping over the arid Great Plains, had followed the Mormons into Utah, the gold hunters into California, and had trailed the fur traders into Oregon.

Room for Everybody

The technique of a motion picture could best describe the migration which wrought this vast sowing and growing of farms across America.

The first scene would be laid in Europe—mainly in Ireland, Scotland, Holland, Germany, Scandinavia, and France. It would present the poverty-stricken and tradition-ironed families of Old Europe listening to talks by agents of the shipping companies. One single theme ran through this propaganda—land! Land for everyone, land that meant prosperity, dignity, freedom. Land was the great magnet that drew the ambitious and the energetic of Northern and Central Europe westward. Homes were sold, household goods auctioned off, families broken apart.

Over the Atlantic these migrants voyaged in an endless stream. Between 1820 and 1830 more than 2,000,000 Europeans came over. In the next decade, 2,600,000 more

arrived.[4] Once here, they joined the rivers of native-born
Americans who were themselves streaming westward. By
oxcart and covered wagon, by flatboat and raft, on horse
and afoot, the settlers moved on and on, following the sun.

For Americans as well as for Europeans, the empty,
fertile lands beyond the mountains were a magical magnet
whose pull many could not resist. Farmers discouraged
by sweating over stony or worn-out soil, townsfolk unhappy or unsuccessful for one reason or another, traders
and professional men seeking still wider fields—together
they went westward.

America Turns Its Back on Europe

Subsequent scenes of this great drama would be laid in
the new States west of the Appalachians. One by one they
sprang into being, with all the confused social, political,
and economic problems the hectic expansion created.

The greatest result of this creation of an inland empire
was not only the establishment of millions of new farms,
and subsequently of mines and industries, but that America turned its back upon Europe. Instead of continuing
our lusty foreign trade, off to such an amazing beginning,
we devoted our energies to the development of our own
continent. We concentrated on the exploitation of land
and wealth, which seemed inexhaustible.

"Busting the prairie sod" changed this nation from a
scattered population in a thin line of thirteen States strung
like beads along the Atlantic coast to a self-centered,
naive mixed people of unlimited potentialities. It was our
fate to have the virgin wealth of a vast continent drop into
our hands like a ripe apple. We were the most fortunate
people in history.

"Westward, Ho!"

In the first few decades of our westward movement the conditions mastered by the settlers were similar to those faced by the first colonists nearly two hundred years previously. Men and women ventured hesitatingly into the forested valleys beyond the mountains, and progress was slow. The Appalachian forests were dense. The wilderness beyond was still walled tightly by imaginative horrors and defended by Indians much more bellicose and far more numerous than those first met along the coast.

But before long conditions changed. The French had explored the Great Lakes, the Ohio, and the Mississippi. The Spanish had wandered from Florida to California. When these areas became part of the new nation, they were not mysterious, unknown fastnesses but areas reasonably well-charted and known, even though they were still unsettled.

Some Americans, indeed, had ventured far beyond the settlements. While their trails merely threaded the vast breadth of the continent, yet their stories did give other Americans an idea of the size and the value of their immense heritage. Hence, as settlers sailed westward over the Great Lakes, floated down the Ohio and Mississippi, poled their way up the Missouri, or plodded behind their covered wagons over dusty, open plains—they did at least know where they were going, how to get there, and what they would find.

While the advancing frontier always repeated the same return to the primitive manner of life that the first colonist farmer experienced, the nineteenth century migrant farmers were not isolated, as had been the first colonists. Back in the seventeenth century the Atlantic rolled

between the settlers and their homes—three thousand miles of stormy emptiness to be crossed, with accompanying hardship and peril. Now, solid land, which could be walked over, linked the frontier with the rest of the nation. The land-link with the East was still far from being perfected, of course. But at least along the rivers and the roads, down the valleys and up over the hills, previous arrivals had established themselves in farm homes which were more numerous and more prosperous year by year.

Instead of cutting free from civilization, the tide of migration followed a leapfrogging method of advance. The first farmers to cross the mountains settled down on the first rich land they reached. The next families to follow settled down just beyond those already established. And so it went, westward, leap by leap, until the continent was spanned.

It must be remembered that America during this period was no longer a land without wheels. Most roads were still very poor, but wagons could roll upon them. Great rivers made broad, smooth highways through the heart of the continent. Railroads were being built and extended westward. The steamboat whistle on the rivers and the locomotive bellow across the prairie were twin voices which shattered the silence of the American wilderness.[5]

Hunters and Fur Traders

Most of the migrants moving westward were farmers. With them went merchants, lawyers, doctors, ministers—practitioners of all the various methods of making a living, who hoped to profit personally by the multitudinous opportunities the newborn States would offer.

But before all these adventured two other types of men,

THE WHITE MAN AND THE INDIAN
Trappers established friendly relations with the Indians
From a painting by Frederick Remington

the fur traders and the lumbermen, the first pioneers of the nineteenth century. Save for the grasslands of the Midwest, most of America was covered with forests in which fur-bearing animals thrived. In Europe and Asia there was such a market for furs that vast profits could be accumulated by traders even after the trappers and hunters had made a living.

How the trappers hated to see the onrush of farming communities! Said one:

"They crowd us out of our hunting grounds. They destroy the forests. We're on the constant run, moving along ahead of the plow and the axe."

Thus by 1800 the sources of American furs, save for the Canadian empire of the Hudson's Bay Company, was well advanced westward. Boston, New York, and Charleston had lost their place in the fur-trading game. Agents at Mobile and Pensacola tapped the Spanish territory, while Buffalo and Montreal served as headquarters for fur traders doing business with American and Canadian hunters around the Great Lakes.

Even with the vast territory at their command, the advance of the farmers by 1830 once again drove the hunters westward. By 1840 there was comparatively little fur trading business left in any of the regions east of the Mississippi Valley.

For a time the professional trapper (Canada again excepted) centered in the region between the Colorado River and the Snake River; but soon, despite territorial disputes between the United States and Canada, the trappers, followed by the traders, erupted into the virgin Oregon territory—their last stand, save for Alaska, which later on became a part of the United States.

"Timber!"

Finally the trappers moved along from the forests, particularly those around the Great Lakes. They left when they had emptied the woodlands of all creatures whose hides could be sold. Then the lumbermen moved in. "Timber!" This was their cry of warning when a tree trembled under the axe and crashed to the earth, and that cry rang through millions of square miles of forest.

Americans were accustomed to the richness of the forests of New England, where pine and spruce were so abundant that they made cities like Bangor in its brief day one of the greatest lumber markets in the world. Yet they were amazed at the treasure house of lumber beyond the Appalachians. The lumbermen found Michigan and Wisconsin particularly wealthy in timber. A fatherly Government gave the priceless forests to the lumbermen at $1.25 an acre, if and when the timber barons bothered to pay even this small price for it.

All at once the greatest lumber boom in the history of the world began. The prairie States were starved for wood —wood for farms, for cities, for factories, wood for everything. Between these markets and the forests were not the narrow and rocky riverways of the East, but the smooth and wide water boulevards of the Great Lakes and the rivers of the prairie States. The hour had struck for one of the greatest private exploitations of a natural resource that the world has ever suffered. The timber kings, that handful of men who bought and stole the forests and sold the lumber, became enormously rich.

Only a few figures are necessary to demonstrate how these lumbermen ravaged the forests. Chicago, the central market and clearinghouse of the lumber boom, in just

one year, 1860, marketed 300,982,207 board feet of soft-wood lumber, 49,102,000,000 laths and 165,927,000,000 shingles.[6] It must be remembered in judging the devastation thus caused that this is but one market and but one year; and that for every item of wood sold at least as much more was wasted—lost in sawdust, lost in transport, or left behind in the woods as butts, slabs, tops, and limbs.

Today, such exploitation of the forests even in commercially minded America would not be possible. Now that most of our forests are gone, we have become interested in conservation and have begun to practice it. But in 1860 there was not even a plan to fight forest fires. There was so much wood in America! We would always have enough—so we thought, then.

And of course wood really was needed. It was vital in the building of America. One contemporary writer of 1836 expressed the situation:[7] "Not to speak of wooden houses, bridges, and roads—of wood for fuel and fencing —we find it adopted in the West for purpose more anomalous, where wooden pins are substituted for nails, and wells are curbed with hollow logs, where the cabin door swinging on wooden hinges is fastened with a wooden latch, and the smoke escapes through a wooden chimney . . . Well may ours be called a wooden country; not merely from the extent of its forests, but because in common use wood has been substituted for a number of the most necessary and common articles—such as stone, iron, and even leather."

Hardship in the West

After the fur trappers had mapped the trails and the lumbermen had provided the material for the homes and

utilities, the farmers came in multitudes to build the inland empire.

Much has been written of the hardship and peril suffered and braved by families on the westward march. Indeed, the facts have been so often romanticized that conditions seem to have been exaggerated. Fatigue, disease, and savages did take a constant toll of the marching myriads, however. This was particularly true in the early days, when roads were hardly more than blazed trails through the forests or ruts across the grasslands. Travel was made excruciating by the bumping and the jolting in the wagons, the cold and rain, the heat and dust.

The trek of the pioneers, however, was rich with color. The white canvas-covered wagons, with their red bodies and huge blue wheels, these rude transports drawn by plodding oxen and laden with the family's most carefully culled possessions—therein lay the raw material of romance. The father, musket in hand, walked ahead of the oxen. The older children, also armed, closed in behind. The mother and the younger children rode upon the springless board that served as a seat. And this journeying continued, mile after mile, day after day, month after month.

But the privations endured cannot be judged by present-day standards. Aside from the few wealthy folk who migrated (they usually traveled by water to New Orleans and then steamed up the rivers to their destinations) most of the migrators were inured to hardship. They welcomed the adventure, and they endured the trials and privation— the price of prosperity in the America of the period.

Americans like to think that civilization came to the United States in full flower with the winning of the Revo-

lution. Nothing could be less true. Eastern cities like Boston, New York, Baltimore, Charleston, and Savannah had a certain amount of culture. All the pleasures of the time were available, if one had the necessary wealth to purchase them. Adjacent to these larger cities and along the rivers which were the natural arteries of trade, there were belts and tiers of prosperous and comfortable farms. But a farmer's prosperity declined in direct proportion to his distance from a city or a river.

Aside from these few favored centers, life in the settled parts of the United States was crude and rough, supported by an agriculture which was miserable. A historian[8] describes the post-Revolutionary farms in these terms: ". . . (they) had but poor and insufficient tools, poor and profitless cattle, poor and meagre crops, and poor and miserable ideas of farming. They had no agricultural journals, no newspapers of any kind, and few books, except the old Family Bible . . . There was little communication from town to town. The facilities for travel were extremely limited . . . Everything was favorable to the growth of prejudice and narrow-minded views. . . ."

So with rich land and the wide opportunities of new States beckoning, what Eastern farmer would hesitate to leave such a life?

Why Move Westward?

Just as in 1600 when land had been the lodestar for the millions of Europeans who swarmed overseas, so it also beckoned brightly in 1800. But the farmers in the Atlantic States already had land—plenty of it. Why then did multitudes of them move westward?

The answer is that many of the first farmers settled (in New England and in much of New York and Pennsylvania) on land that was not then and is not even now worth farming.

Today much of this land, dotted by the cellar-holes of abandoned homesteads, is reverting to woodland and pasture—its proper economic use.

In the early decades of the nineteenth century the farm families eked out a bitter life on this poor soil. Two centuries had drained what little fertility much of it had originally possessed. The farmers were tired of blunting their tools and their souls upon the stony earth, which now was impoverished as well.

In the South, the tendency to evacuate and begin all over again on new land was not so prevalent as in the North. Yet the need for potash of the tobacco plant and the vicious cycle of more and ever more land by King Cotton, plus the political and economic need of the South for more slave States, urged the Southern farmer to move westward, too.

There were other and broader forces driving farmers westward. First, there was the long series of territorial acquisitions which filled out this nation's breadth to the Pacific. No nation was ever blessed so rapidly with so much empty land.

Second, the various land policies of the Federal Government not merely made it possible for any man with an ounce of "git-up-and-git" in his system to acquire a homestead, but also fostered a wildfire of land speculation. In addition to the actual settlement and development of the continent, the area was sold and resold, developed and redeveloped, not once, but many times—on paper. This

process worked to the enrichment of a few speculators and to the hardship of nearly everyone else concerned.

Third, the condition of the nation's commerce and finance after the Revolution, after the Embargo and during various panics, so depressed business and trade that many an unemployed man naturally left home to make a place for himself under the western sky.

Finally, the constant, if irregular, development of industry and commerce and the tremendous growth of the population of the United States created expanding markets for farm products. More and more, people in the East turned from the land to other activities. They needed food and ever more food, and Europe was hungry for food, also. So there was a market for all the food that all the farms America might develop could produce.

[1] Riegel, Robert E. *America Moves West*. New York. 1930
[2, 3, 4] Edwards, Everett E. *U. S. Dept. of Agri. Yearbook*. 1940
[5] Clark, William H. *Railroads and Rivers*. Boston. 1939
[6] Kirkland, E. C. *History of American Economic Life*. New York. 1932
[7] Hall, James. *Statistics of the West*. Cincinnati. 1836
[8] Flint, C. L. *American Agriculture*. In 21st Annual Report of the Secretary of the Massachusetts Board of Agriculture. Boston. 1874

CHAPTER XI

LAND POLICIES

THE STORY of how the United States Government parceled out many millions of acres of land is a vast and amazing tangle.

The first great wave of migration westward went through New York State and Pennsylvania into the old Northwest—the area between the Ohio river, the Great Lakes, and the Mississippi. Most of this region had been given over to the Confederation of the States by various of the thirteen colonies (States) which had claimed it under original charters from the Crown. The Continental Congress opened this area to settlement by means of the famous Ordinances of 1785 and 1787.

Some 2,000,000 acres were at once purchased with depreciated Revolutionary soldiers' certificates by a group of speculators known as the Ohio Company. Several million more acres were purchased by the Scioto Company, a group of Congressmen. A third group that also undertook settlement of the Northwest was the Symmes Company.[1]

Indian troubles created by British agents held up survey of the area, and settlers were forbidden to enter the region. But in December 1787 a group of adventurers from Ipswich, Massachusetts, trekked overland, arriving six months later at Marietta, Ohio. Farmers from New

142

Jersey settled along the Little Miami River. A number of Virginians and families from Connecticut also arrived in the vicinity.

At the same time, Vermont and western New York were settled. Many families came up from western Pennsylvania and New Jersey, and some pushed northward into New Hampshire and northeastward into Maine. After 1800 the migration began to assume larger proportions. Families from New England, New York, Virginia, and Carolina swarmed westward in ever-increasing numbers. By 1803 Ohio had been admitted into the Union, and, in order, Indiana, Illinois, and Michigan followed.

The settlement of the Southern States between the mountains and the Mississippi followed upon the invention of the cotton gin. Tennessee soon had a millon inhabitants. Alabama and Mississippi became the heart of the cotton empire.

The Louisiana Purchase increased the area of the United States by 140 per cent. Under Napoleon only a few thousands of persons inhabited the vast area, and half of them were Americans. Soon hundreds of cotton planters from the Old South followed the fur traders into this section. The American pre-emption of Texas brought on the war with Mexico and resulted in the acquisition of more land. Another great empire had been added to the United States.

Then came the discovery of gold in California in 1849 and the boom which transformed that former Mexican-Spanish pastoral region into a State almost overnight. The Oregon Territory was finally acquired, adding still another vast area to the United States.

The problem of disposing of all this land was one of the

most important and the most serious the Federal Government has ever faced.

The Northwest Territory

The clamor and the confusion was great. The Ordinance of 1785 was perhaps the fundamental attempt in solving the situation, even though frankly experimental in intent. It created the rectangular survey system—the division of public lands into townships six miles square and the subdivisions of each township into thirty-six lots of 640 acres each (one square mile). In each township, Lot Number Sixteen was assigned for school purposes. Later on, Lot Number Thirty-Six usually was set aside in similar manner.

The land could all be bought at one dollar the acre. Later, the standard minimum price of land rose variously and held to a minimum of a dollar and a quarter an acre until the Homestead Act of 1862.

Then came the Ordinance of 1787, which was of immeasurable importance both politically and agriculturally. It arranged for the organization and government of the Northwest Territory. It provided that new lands should be organized into independent States and not become appendages of States already organized. This prevented the growth of old States at the expense of their neighbors and so limited the political ambitions of the original thirteen colonies.

This ordinance laid down the legal principles under which real property was acquired, held, conveyed, and inherited. In particular, primogeniture, that relic of feudalism, was abolished. This was a radical departure from colonial law. It "determined the form of land ownership

THE YANKEE PEDDLER
He brought news and goods to backwoods farms

n.

throughout the entire West; and even the older States, in which certain relics of feudal tenure still survived, have since remodelled their land laws after the pattern set by this Ordinance." [2]

The original land policy (of 1785) had the fatal fault of limiting purchase of public lands to families that were comparatively wealthy. Few farmers had the $640 necessary to pay for a farm. This fault was aggravated in 1800, when the price was doubled. The reason for the charge was that the Federal Government considered the public lands as its revenue-producing property.

There was plenty of agitation. "Public lands ought to be given free to farmers who will settle on them, build homes, and till the soil," clamored many Americans.

"That's ridiculous," cried others. "Nobody should have land unless he pays for it!"

As a sop to the demands for free land, the Act of 1800 made it possible for farmers to buy half or quarter sections—320 acres or 160 acres. Also, the Act provided a credit system. A man could buy his section or fraction of a section, pay down one quarter of the price, and then pay the balance in equal annual instalments. This served to stimulate settlement of the Northwest Territory. While by 1800, only 1,484,087 acres[3] had been sold, by 1820, thanks to the credit system, some 18,000,000 acres had been purchased.[4]

However, this credit system was a mixed blessing.

"I can't market my produce, and so I can't meet my annual payments," said one farmer.

"The worst of it is," said another, "the banks down East and elsewhere have made loans to lots of us to finance our trips out here. They're already beginning to foreclose on

those of us who can't pay. We're making as big a holler as we can."

To prevent an open outbreak of indignant violence, Congress passed various relief measures, all merely palliative. But Congress finally did adjust the situation. The Act of 1820 allowed farmers to retain a portion of their farms in direct ratio to the amount they had already paid up. The balance of the debt was canceled by letting the portion of the farms not yet covered by payment revert to the Government. Thus the Federal Government took back from the farmers some 2,500,000 acres.[5] To prevent further trouble, the credit system was also abolished.

Squatters

The next development in our national land policy was concerned with the legalization of squatters' titles.

Legally, land title could not be acquired until the Government survey had been completed and the price of the land paid to the United States Treasury. But the surveyors lagged far behind the settlers; so multitudes of families simply moved into the wilderness, selected the land they wanted, and started farming.

Rich only in ambition and energy, these families were squatters. Legally, they could be evicted as soon as the surveyors caught up with them. But there were so very many of these squatters that Congress quailed at the storm of protest their eviction would cause. So the politicians evolved the system of land title known as "pre-emption." It is a tortuous subject, as are most governmental adjustments that are developed to meet accomplished facts. Essentially, pre-emption meant that the squatter could buy the land he was using by paying the price originally set

per acre by the Government. It simply became a matter of "deferred payment."

Land speculators, especially Easterners, did not like the new system. The squatters in many sections had occupied the best lands. This cut into the profits the speculators had hoped to garner through buying those good lands and holding them for higher resale prices. The speculators put up a fight.

The squatters themselves fought back. As soon as their holdings were included in new States, they voted in State legislation that would control the speculators. This they could do, because squatters were a decided majority.

The Policy Liberalized

After 1841 Congress began taking a more liberal policy towards the disposal of public lands. First, there was the gift of public lands to stimulate public improvements, such as roads, canals, bridges, schools, and railroads. By 1861 (in twenty years) Congress had followed out this policy to the extent of giving away some sixty millions of acres to individuals and some 105,131,000 acres to States for "purposes other than internal improvements."

Of the 269,000,000 acres taken from the public domain in 1841-1861, only 68,752,889 acres were sold. Congress gave away the rest.[6]

Because of this development of land policy, the coming of the Civil War found the old Northwest Territory well settled. It was dotted with prosperous farms, important cities, and many flourishing industrial centers. Out of nothing, within a single lifetime of seventy years, the States of Ohio, Indiana, Illinois, Michigan, Minnesota, and Iowa had been created. To a lesser degree the new

States of Missouri and Kansas had also been established by this first great wave of migration.

These States were predominately settled by New Englanders, with some mixtures from New York, New Jersey, and Pennsylvania. Thus they became free States, as opposed to slave States—an important contribution to the preservation of the United States.

The South Migrates

Settlement of the area south of the old Northwest Territory—Kentucky, Tennessee, Alabama, Mississippi, Louisiana, Texas, and Arkansas—was similar to that in the North. In fact, migration into Kentucky and Tennessee came even earlier than that into Ohio. Farmers started straggling through the passes of the Blue Ridge and the Great Smoky Mountains before the Revolution and continued even during that struggle. By 1790, for example, Kentucky had some 70,000 inhabitants and Tennessee had around 36,000.

These were small farmers, many from Pennsylvania and others from Virginia and Carolina. Thus, although the leadership, politically and economically, of the two States continued in the hands of the so-called Southern aristocracy, most of the citizens of these States had been well-established small farmers before King Cotton came to reign. Their sympathies were strongly for the Union and, when the test came in 1861, the small farmers were numerous enough to keep their States on the side of the Union.

The migration was of sharply different character in the South—in Alabama, Mississippi, across into Louisiana and Texas, up into Arkansas, and to a lesser degree

into Oklahoma (Indian Territory), Kansas, and Missouri. First, there had been the settlement of "poor whites" driven ever westward by the pressure of capitalistic cotton planters. Gradually, as King Cotton's reign extended, the cotton planters followed westward from the seaboard States.

Thus arose not only the political difference between the two new sections but also the economic difference. In the North, while farming still remained important, the ambitious New England stock turned to industry, built efficient railroads, and established themselves solidly on the road to complete economic balance. In the South, thanks to King Cotton and in a lesser degree to tobacco and to cattle ranching (this last particularly in Texas), the economic system remained predominately agricultural.

In the North, capital began to be accumulated, and internal development was rapid and secure. The people were almost all white and characteristically independent. Development was strikingly even, and few inequalities existed. In the South, the contrary prevailed. Migration itself was a helter-skelter scramble. For example: "In this newly developed cotton belt, a pell-mell regime prevailed in a scrambling and scattered mass of many sorts of people, planters, slaves, farmers, poor whites, and frontiersmen, all concerned with getting cotton lands." [7]

The Louisiana Territory

It required many years before the full opportunity of the vast outer reaches of the Louisiana Territory were appreciated by Americans. The reason was that early Americans believed the region beyond the Mississippi was a great desert!

After Lewis and Clark made their epic journey, and after Zebulon Pike reached Colorado, it still took time for the great truth to filter eastward. For many years the Great Plains were merely a highway between the East and the Pacific coast. Later, migration erupted westward like a tidal wave. In general, it continued in two parallel streams. One flowed from the old Northwest Territory; the other from the slave States.

The expansion westward from the Northern States waited for the opening of the Oregon Territory. In the same manner, the expansion west from the slave States waited for the conclusion of the troubles with Mexico. Space in both areas was so vast that complete settlement waited for the completion of the railroads.

California

Settlers had displayed some hesitation in venturing across the plains to the Rockies and then in clambering over that rocky wall. But California was beginning to be settled from the direction of the sea, even while Mexican domination continued.

Ships from Boston and New York had frequented the coast for fifty years before the '49 gold stampede. Sailors brought out cargoes of manufactured goods and traded with the Spanish dons and the Mexican ranchers for leather and hides. Thus, small American settlements were well-established in such areas as the San Joaquin Valley and the Sacramento Valley. A few Yankees married Spanish heiresses and so won control of some large ranches. All this was accomplished before westward-moving America had scarcely more than crossed the Mississippi river.

Accordingly, after the Mexican War, California fell into American hands like a ripe apple. It was more American anyhow, than Mexican, even before this border war was fought.

Then came Gold and the greatest stampede in history— over the continent in covered wagons, down the Atlantic coast by ship to Panama, over the Isthmus by land, and then by ship again up the Pacific coast; and also around the Horn in the bright glory of the marvelous clipper ships Donald McKay built at East Boston. Later, in 1850, California became an established State which drew farmers and other settlers to the Pacific, taking away from the less favored mountain States a considerable number of their inhabitants.

The Homestead Act

Thus, by 1860 America was a continent "settled" from shore to shore. Railroads had come into being. Good transportation was available to the tremendous areas passed over during the first washing of the wave of migration westward. The outlines of many of America's States were hardly more than sketched, of course, but the railroads soon made a mighty difference.

Because of our passion for land, the need of King Cotton's enlargement of his empire, the hard times and depressions along the Eastern shore, the greed of land speculators, and the successive openings of vast territory, we had spread ourselves rather thinly from shore to shore. Waves of native Americans were increasingly reinforced by tidal torrents from Europe. America was on the march, filling in the white spaces left on its map.

To this, at about Civil War time, the extension of the

railroads added the final touch of good transportation which could be stretched almost to any place where future profits loomed. The steel rail was a magic wand which created farms, towns, and cities almost anywhere.

As an example of the development of America's migration: "De Tocqueville calculated (1830) the rate of western progress at nineteen miles per annum. At this moment (1856) it must be reckoned by hundreds of miles. . . . I believe there is nothing in history to compare with this seven-league progress of civilization."[8]

Then finally came the Homestead Act in 1862. It was one of the most important items of legislation ever passed in Washington concerning the development of our nation. It gave free to any real settler, a quarter section—160 acres of land. This gift from his country had only one string tied to it. The man had to live on his desired land for five years.

This Act was the American land policy. It climaxed years of struggle between landlordism, speculators, and Federal financial policy on the one side—and individual proprietorship on the other. With this Act, America came of age. The stage was set for the future triumph of American agriculture.

[1] *History of the Public Land Policies*. New York. 1939
[2] Carver, T. N. *Bailey's Cyclopedia of American Agriculture*. New York. 1909
[3, 4, 5, 6] Bogart, E. L. *Op. cit.*
[7] Phillips, U. B. *Plantation and Frontier, Documentary History of American Industrial Society*. Cleveland. 1910
[8] Sterling, James. *Letters from the Slave States*. London. 1857

CHAPTER XII

FROM SCRUB TO PEDIGREE

INSIDE the great tent which housed the Hartford County Fair in Connecticut in the year 1840, Henry Colman, one of the first leading farm educators, pleaded with the farmers to give better care to their cattle.

"You give them little protection in winter," he cried. "Even with snow heaped upon their backs, you feed them only the poor hay of the pasture. The result is what might be expected. There is nothing more painful to see than the withered, lean, lanthorn-visaged condition in which your stock generally comes out in the Spring . . ."[1]

Such farmers as bothered to read agricultural journals at that time would find editorial articles containing words like these: "(the farmers' cattle) are a mixture of every breed . . . not celebrated for any one thing; some of them are good milkers, as far as quantity is concerned, but as to quality of the milk and aptitude to fatten, they generally fail. Their calves are of diminutive size . . . and, if reared, of slow growth, seldom coming in until the third year . . . They are small, short-bodied, thin, coarse-haired, steep-rumped, slab-sided, having little aptitude to fatten or to lay the fat in the right place."[2]

Here are expressed the two faults of early American animal husbandry: The farmer neglected to feed and to

153

care for his creatures properly; and he did not bother to improve his breeds.

Horses, save those used for riding and by military officers, were treated with a brutality the present day cannot imagine. They were fed barely enough to keep them on their feet, and were driven with whip and spur. When they collapsed, they were left to die, for a few dollars would buy another unfortunate beast. About the most valuable part of a horse was the hide, which was made into leather.

Beginning early in the nineteenth century, humanitarians began to orate upon kindness to animals. These gentlefolk were soon joined by hardheaded farmers and business men who saw the dollars-and-cents value of feeding an animal so that more could be taken out of him. Soon every farmer in America, short of the frontier, was urged to treat his beasts better. This might have had but limited effects upon American animal husbandry, but two other influences were at work. These were the improvement of stock through breeding and the development of stock raising from a haphazard, part-time job to a major division of American economic life.

Breeding

The United States, like England, has been fortunate in that men of means, established as leaders in other fields, interested themselves as amateurs in certain forms of agriculture, particularly in animal breeding. Wealthy men devoted themselves to "improving the breed"— whether horses, cattle, pigs, or hens. Amateurs in the art, they characteristically employed experts to do the work. They spent unlimited dollars in importing the best sires the world afforded. They operated their stables, barns,

and sheds with the most meticulous attention to detail and created new blood lines which have been of incalculable value to the entire nation.

The years preceding 1860 saw not only the development of these amateurs but also of professional breeders. These experts have contributed much to the improvement of American livestock.

There have of recent years been two other forces at work for the improvement of stock. First, there is the Federal Government. This is one legitimate function of government which, long neglected, has at last been properly assumed. Second, there are the farmers' organizations, such as the Grange and the important and popular 4-H clubs, which teach and demonstrate the value of pedigreed stock over scrub.

Hogs

Hogs were not much improved by breeding during this period. Some sires were imported, boars of the Berkshire breed in particular coming over from Europe. But native sows were almost uniformly used. The improvement from the razor-backed swine of colonial days came about through housing and better feeding.[3]

Farmers stopped permitting their pigs to run wild and forage in the forest. Instead, they fattened them in pens. As a result, the razor-like leanness vanished, and the creatures became cylinders of fat.

Much of the porcine revolution was completed about 1840. A writer of the period declares:[4] "Formerly New England was over-run with a lank-sided race of animals (pigs) which devoured the substance of the farmer, and like Pharoah's lean kine, 'were still ill-favored and lean

as before,' and whose chief return to the owner was skin, bone, and bristle. But we think we may now congratulate . . . on the almost entire extinction of this race . . . We now generally find small-boned, well-porportioned breeds of swine . . ."

Cattle

The interest of wealthy amateurs was particularly effective with cattle. Only horses have been more favored by amateurs. Pedigreed cattle were items of concern to Social Registerites of New York and of Philadelphia just before 1850. The annual cattle auctions, especially if pure-blood stock was on the block, became high lights of the social season. Men distinguished in finance and industry vied with one another to acquire the best animals.

The improvement of cattle by these amateurs and by professional breeders, as well as by some enlightened individual farmers, began as early as 1783. The importations by Miller and Gough to Virginia and Maryland in 1783 were apparently Shorthorns. The so-called Patton stock of the Matthew-Patton family of importers were also Shorthorns. About 1812, Shorthorns again came into popularity. The Massachusetts Society For Promoting Agriculture distinguished itself in importing this stock.

It really was not until 1840, however, that American farmers in general gave serious attention to improving their stock. Scrubs were still in evidence everywhere. As an example of the cattle which even Yankee farmers were producing after two hundred years, the 1841 records of the Brighton Abattoir, near Boston, show that cows weighed an average of 450 pounds, steers but 600 pounds, and oxen only 875 pounds.[5] Even after the value of better

A New England Dairy Farm

Courtesy Maine Development Commission

stock and better care had been forcefully expounded, many farmers were stubborn about continuing the colonial methods of husbandry handed down through the generations.

"If it was good enough for my father, it's good enough for me," was a common argument.

However, circumstances developed soon which compelled a change. Originally, farmers had no need of distinguishing between beef and milk production. Dairy farming was a specialty no farmer considered. There was no market for milk. Butter and cheese were locally produced, usually by the farm wife, and locally consumed.

But by 1840 or so the Middle West bgan to produce beef cattle, which were driven over the mountains to eastern markets. By 1850, thanks to the railroads, western beef was transported cheaply enough so that it undersold the local eastern supply. Thus the eastern farmer, especially in New England and New York, turned by necessity to dairy farming. He found his lush pastures, poor though the soil was, ideal for this type of agriculture.

Another development was the industrialization of the Northeast and the rapid growth of cities, creating a booming market for fluid milk. The development of railroads made it possible for fresh milk to be rushed to the market —however unsanitary the methods of retailing and production.

The production of fluid milk did not grow to prominence overnight, of course. Much butter and cheese also was made locally, since the cities were a growing market also for them. But in time the fluid milk market became a vast business. To consider only one example, farmers near Boston found it so profitable to sell only milk in that

city that they quit making butter and cheese. The remoter dairy sections, such as Wisconsin, took over the cheese and butter production and monopolized the canned-milk field later on.

Thus, in general, beef cattle vanished from the Northeast, and dairy herds took their place. A scrub cow is a very poor milk-producing machine. The farmers were compelled by solid dollars-and-cents argument to improve their herds, to feed them better, and to give them better care.

The result is indicated by a few figures. As early as 1840, dairying in the United States was already well-established. That year, dairy products were worth $33,-787,000.[6] That is hardly a drop in the bucket compared with today's totals; but for a time it was a magnificent beginning. Butter records show how the production increased. In 1850 the production was 313,345 pounds;[7] in 1860 it was 459,681 pounds.[8]

The improvement of milking cattle was featured by the importation of such famous European breeds as the Jersey, the Ayrshire, and the Holstein. More and more farmers paid attention to their stock. Today, good blood is relatively common in all progressive herds. While some farmers do not bother to lay out money for pedigreed stock or the service of a blue-ribbon bull, yet there is no farmer in the milk business who is not aware of the difference which better stock can make in his monthly milk check.

Sheep

The development of sheep follows a course in this period similar to that of cattle, with the difference that

sheep raising was featured by a series of strange booms and enthusiasms followed by declines almost as marked.

Until about 1807, sheep were relatively unimportant in America. Farmers continued to run a few sheep as a matter of course. Most of the wool so produced was consumed locally. Clothing was home-grown until the development of the textile mills somewhat later.

Mutton, save as cheap food on the farm, was of low value in most American markets. In Europe, mutton was the cheapest and commonest of meat and was thus stigmatized as peasants' fare. In America, where every man was his brother's equal, it was a confession of poverty to buy mutton. If you raised your own, however, it was natural enough to eat it to save it from going to waste.

Then in 1807 came the Embargo and the related shipping controls. This Act forbade American ships to engage in foreign trade and thus deprived America of European manufactured goods. Cheap woolen fabrics usually imported from Europe, particularly from England, were cut off. So a market for wool was created in American cities and towns, the American wool-weaving industry took on importance, and the farmer discovered that sheep could become another money crop.

Precisely at this very time when America needed wool, Robert Livingstone began importing Merino sheep for his New York estate. Others quickly followed his lead. The Merino, a Spanish breed, had long been famous for its excellence as a wool producer. The Spanish Crown, however, strictly forbade the exportation of this sheep. It took the Napoleonic wars to create empty pockets in Spain, and then Americans again could import the famous sheep.

Merino wool sold in the United States for about two dollars a pound, in contrast with domestic wool, which seldom reached fifty cents a pound. Thus, by 1810, when Livingstone had developed a Merino herd, he was able to sell rams at $1000 each.[9]

This news vastly stimulated the importation of Merino sheep. Great herds soon became established everywhere in the East; and the craze for Merinos mushroomed like a Florida real-estate boom until 1816. Then the bubble collapsed. Instead of two dollars a pound, Merino wool in October of 1816 brought but sixty-eight cents; and in July of 1821 but fifty-seven cents.[10]

But another sheep boom was even then in the making. This time it was the Saxony breed. By 1822 there was a great demand for this longer-legged, finer-boned, and more delicate variety of the Merino that had been developed in Saxony. This second boom failed to reach the extent of the first. Not only did wool prices fail to rise to their former levels after the slump, but smart salesmen foisted off all sorts of scrub sheep to ignorant farmers under the label of "Saxony." The farmers did not know the difference—until too late. This gave the Saxony breed a poor reputation.

Meanwhile, a market was at last developing for mutton. As wool producers alone, sheep were not profitable, on the average; but when meat was combined with wool, then sheep were very profitable.

As meat production became increasingly important, farmers began to import still better breeds. The New Leicester and the Bakewell (probably the same breed) were brought over from England. This meat production enjoyed a steady and sane development, gradually moving

westward with the frontier until it became established on its own economically favored grounds in the West. This establishment did not take place without opposition from the cattlemen, however, who claimed that sheep ruined the grazing range.

In the East, wool production was still to enjoy its third and last boom. By 1830 the need of American mills for wool and the vast development of an American market for wool cloth, incident to the growth of population, set wool prices soaring once more. Once again wool offered the farmers easy money. Herds spread over New England, New York, and Pennsylvania, until by 1840 there were 19,331,374 head of sheep in America. The greatest concentrations were in Vermont, the Berkshires of Massachusetts, and the very considerable pasture areas of New York and Pennsylvania.[11]

"The farmers are no longer growing wheat, corn, or potatoes!" announced the alarmed newspapers of the day.

"We'll have to import everything we eat from Ohio— and pay through the nose for it," gloomed city folks in the East.

"These farmers will never learn that sheep ruin the land," declared real estate dealers.

Officials were no less alarmed. Wrote one:[12] "Persons . . . who worked for the wool-mad farmers. They asked for money for their labor, but money was not to be had because the clipping of wool, owing to the derangements of business, had not been sold. They asked to receive their pay in grain; but the wool farmer had abandoned all cultivation for sheep husbandry. They asked for their pay in pork, but the farmers who raised no grain could raise no pork . . ."

Inevitably, the wool fever finally worked its own cure. As one farmer's wife complained then: "Our wool isn't bringing in enough to cover the cost of raising the sheep. There's too much wool on the market! Everybody's got wool to sell."

The farmers knew that with pockets empty they'd have to begin raising their own food again, or starve. Consequently, soon after 1840, another sheep craze was all but ended. A few sheep continued to be grazed on the hill pastures of the Northeast for generations (there are still a few flocks to be seen) ; but after 1850, at the latest, sheep growing had faded once again and has never again become important.

By that time the sheep farmer was well on his way west. Ohio was his center at about 1850; and after the Civil War sheep crossed the Mississippi and were eating the grass of the Great Plains.

Poultry

Modern-type poultry farms were not organized in the period between the Revolution and the Civil War. During this time, colonial methods of poultry care persisted. The farmer generally kept a few dozens of hens, ducks, and geese for home use—for eggs, feathers, and meat. The farmer's wife probably had her "egg-money" franchise; but then it was mostly a matter of trading extra eggs at the local general store for what few luxuries she could obtain or afford.

Wild turkeys were still plentiful; and wild ducks, geese, and other wild fowl were so abundant that they provided plenty of meat. Pot-hunters made a regular business of slaughtering these wild fowl and supplying the city mar-

SHEEP ARE RETURNING TO NEW ENGLAND FARMS

kets. Thus for many years the farm flocks were not of economic importance. They were merely private adjuncts to the farm table.

But as the population of the United States increased, as markets developed, and wild game vanished near the big towns, poultry began to grow in importance. By 1840, Rhode Island was something of a center, thanks to the many textile mills in its area and in near-by Massachusetts. New York and Pennsylvania farmers also found poultry profitable. The 1840 Federal census discovered that poultry products were being marketed to the value of $9,344,000.

Unlike sheep and cattle, poultry held its own in the East as the decades rolled along. Poultry raising also developed in Ohio, Illinois, and Wisconsin, for example—and in California much later. But poultry raising in this period remained primitive and of comparatively little importance, save locally.

Crops and Livestock

This between-the-wars period very clearly demonstrates one great feature of American agriculture, that crops and livestock were interdependent, especially in the northern States, since in the South, cotton was the leading product.

Take the westward progression of wheat. In colonial times and until 1820 or so, New York and Pennsylvania produced most of America's wheat. Then Ohio took the leadership about 1830-40; and by 1850, Indiana, Illinois, and Wisconsin were in the van. Similarly, corn production followed the pioneering farmers westward. In general,

it followed the same route, although tending to lie in a belt somewhat to the south of the wheat belt.

The farmers at first feared to undertake the cultivation of the prairie sod.

"Look at these wide open, windswept spaces!" whispered the women to each other. "There's no wood for building. We'll have to live in sod houses."

"How will we keep our cattle together, when we haven't any wood for fences, either?" the men asked each other. "And drive your pickax into this prairie sod. Tough as woven leather!"

But the steel plow finally broke the sod, cheap barbed wire fenced in the fields, and the exploitation of the forests to the North provided wood for building and fuel. The prairies were conquered; and the great corn sections of Iowa, Nebraska, and part of Kansas came into being.

This shifting of corn and wheat from the older States to the West worked important changes. Instead of general farming, each Eastern section tended to specialize in crops best suited to its climate and soil. (Always, however, some of the subsistence type of small farm has remained.)

Market gardening developed amazingly in the immediate areas about Boston, Providence, New York, and Philadelphia. Dairy farms came into being where soils were poor, water abundant, and transportation to city markets available. Onions and leaf tobacco, as examples of specialized farm products, spread up the Connecticut River Valley. In New York State, hops and grapes became important.

Meanwhile, the farm family no longer needed to be entirely self-sufficient. Given cash crops, the farmer could buy "store" clothes, furniture, and tools. Household

industries declined in proportion as industrialization increased.

The East had passed from an agricultural economic to a wage-earning status. While the Eastern farmer was adjusting himself to industrialization, the Western farmer became his competitor, not alone in wheat and corn, but in meat. For years, as in the Connecticut Valley, cattle were fattened with surplus corn for the Boston market. In the same way, eastern New York fed cattle for New York City; and southeastern Pennsylvania did a like service for Philadelphia.

But into this business, which occupied an important part of the farm economy in the East, consuming surplus corn, came competition from the West. Out in the new corn States, despite the Erie Canal and the railroads concentrating upon Chicago, there was a vast surplus of very cheap corn. It had to be concentrated for economical shipment to the East.

Whiskey was one such concentrate. For its bulk, it was very valuable. Hogs and cattle were the second, because animals consumed the corn, changed it into meat, and went to market on their own four legs. Pig-driving soon became an important business. Vast herds of the creatures made their slow, dusty way southward to the cotton plantations and eastward to the cities of the coast.

The drovers grumbled. "These herds can't make more than about ten miles a day," said one. "The pigs lose weight very rapidly, day by day on the roads. The trip is too much for them."

A little later, these men spoke more cheerfully. "Railroads have come into the corn belt," they explained. "To-day we fence in the pigs among the cornfields. We fatten

them up; and then they ride east to the slaughterhouses in boxcars."

Even this changed in time as Chicago and other cities established packing houses. It was cheaper to send dressed meat east than to ship the live animals. The meat was packed near the cornfields because of the economic gain.

Cattle were also driven eastward over the mountains in huge herds. Ohio in particular, from around 1810, sent great drives eastward.

Cattle production belongs traditionally to the wide-open spaces. Thus, progressively, the cattle-raising sections moved on ahead of the frontiers of the farmers. Particularly in Texas and adjacent States, cattle barons found plenty of room, for a time, to range their beasts, and created a veritable cattle empire.

To market their beasts, they organized great cattle drives to railheads, the western terminals of roads reaching down from the corn belt. There, the steers were taken away to be fattened for the packing houses. A few figures tell the story of this removal of cattle raising and corn growing from the East to the West. In 1850 the United States census found only 660,000 head of cattle in Texas; in 1860, the number was 2,760,000. As for corn, it was about fifty cents a bushel in the East and but ten cents a bushel in Iowa. Thus did the westward march of agriculture change the farm habits of the East—robbing that section of corn and cattle.

The Patient Ox

No single item better epitomizes the development of agriculture in this seventy-year period than the passing of the ox, the strongest of draught animals.

In colonial days, and for most of the first half of the nineteenth century, the ox was vitally important in the Northeast. This docile creature broke up the virgin soil; dragged away stumps; pulled stoneboats laden with hundreds of pounds of stones levered from the fields; and hauled crops to markets over the first crude roads. Horses were too weak, too nervous, and too expensive to keep, in proportion to their strength, for such work.

Then conditions changed. The roughest work of establishing farms was ended. Roads were improved. There came the need for speed rather than for brute strength. So the ox had served his purpose, and the lighter but faster horse came into his place.

In addition there was the innovation of farm machinery. Machines cost money; and to get the necessary return for them, they had to be operated as near capacity as possible. So the horse, harnessed to mowers, reapers, cultivators, harrows, binders, and the rest, walked into almost every farm. One man could finish as much work with a horse as two men with an ox apiece could do.

After 1860, oxen vanished. Many a farmer today has never seen an ox. To his children they are merely something their grandfather dimly remembers as once being used on the farm. An ox is a museum piece—it is one with the spinning wheel and the passenger pigeon.

[1] Colman, Henry. Addresses at Norwich, New Haven, and Hartford, Conn., at the County Cattle Shows in the year 1840. Boston. 1840
[2] The Cultivator. Albany, N. Y. 1839
[3] Gras, N. S. B. A History of Agriculture. New York. 1925
[4] New England Farmer. XI. Boston. 1833
[5] Fourth Report. Massachusetts Board of Agriculture. Boston. 1841
[6, 7, 8, 11] United States Census Reports, 1840, 1850, 1860, 1840
[9] U. S. Bureau of Animal Industry. Special Report on Sheep Industry. 1892
[10] Bogart. Op. Cit. Quoting New York Shipping Lists. 1816—et seq.
[12] Report of the Secretary, Massachusetts Board of Agriculture. Boston. 1838

CHAPTER XIII

APPLESEED JOHNNY

THROUGH the forests and the fields of the old Northwest Territory, for some forty years beginning about 1801, a weird figure shambled, and always alone. Poorly dressed, this man wandered about among the early settlements and the Indian tribes, eating and sleeping where best he might.

He carried two bags, one filled with crudely printed little Bibles, which he gave away. He was a missionary, and he preached to white men and Indians alike. The other bag was filled with apple seeds. Wherever he went, he planted a few seeds in likely spots. The Indians were certain he was possessed of a Spirit. They respected and even honored him. Even through the bloody and bitter War of 1812, when British-instigated savages slaughtered Americans, this man walked at peace.

John Chapman was born in Springfield, Massachusetts, in 1775. Far and wide this strange pomologist became famous as "Appleseed Johnny." He died in Indiana and was buried beneath an apple tree with one of his little Bibles, opened at the Beatitudes, in his hands.

During his forty years of wandering, Appleseed Johnny must have planted thousands of trees. Before 1840, few farmers bothered to grow fruit to sell. Yet, even from the earliest days, American farmers who were interested in fruit for their own use imported many trees from Europe. This was especially true in New England.

William Blackstone, the first white farmer at Boston, the mysterious recluse who anticipated the Puritans at Boston by at least ten years, planted an orchard on the south side of what is now Beacon Hill—perhaps on what is now Boston Common.[1] The Puritans grew apples and brought over trees from England for their farms. John Winthrop, the first Governor of the Massachusetts Bay Colony, is said to have planted a large orchard on what is now Governor's Island in Boston Harbor.

This New England tradition of fine fruit growing continued and, from 1829 on, the Massachusetts Horticultural Society, founded that year, did much to advance it. The Society held fruit shows each fall, just as it stages flower shows today. One of its specific aims was to encourage the development of better fruit, both by the introduction of fruits from abroad and by popularizing superior varieties. Similarly, in New York and in Pennsylvania, men of means also labored to stimulate fruit growing. The original parents of most varieties of fruit even now grown in this country were introduced from abroad.[2]

Here, European varieties were not propagated generally by modern methods, which would have kept them true to form, but by seed. Thus, since no two seedlings were ever alike, a tremendous if unwitting development took place. Authorities estimate that as a result of this seed-propagating habit of the early American farmer, from eighty-five to ninety per cent of our important fruits have been obtained as naturally occurring seedlings.[3] In most instances neither parent is known.

Well into the nineteenth century, the efforts of gentleman farmers to introduce superior fruits was mainly a

labor of love. Much really good fruit was grown, mostly in and around the larger Eastern cities, but such fruit was a garden crop rather than a farm crop.

One reason for the general lack of interest in fruit by the majority of farmers was that they regarded it primarily as raw material for beverages. Some fruit was eaten, of course, but only locally. Instead, apples went into cider and applejack, pears into "perry" and brandy, peaches into brandy, and grapes into wine and brandy.

Every farm had its cider press. Oceans of perry (pear cider) were pressed out each fall and then allowed to ferment in cherished barrels until sufficiently "hard." Here and there, farmers had little stills from which they made a "white lightning" brandy from fermented perry or from peaches.

Some fruit was grown as a cheap means of feeding to livestock, although probably not often to milking cows. Official testimony exists concerning this practice: "The planting of apple orchards was recommended for the single purpose of feeding apples to hogs, to beef cattle, or even to milch cows." [4]

However, by about 1840, farmers generally began to take an interest in growing fruit for marketing. Transportation made it possible to ship the fruit to the cities, and the increased urban population created an expanding market for it. As a result, nurseries appeared to supply fairly good trees of superior stock—even budded and grafted stock. And by 1850 good orchards were common in New England. However, most Yankees failed then as now to take fruit growing seriously, despite the fact that New England apples (Baldwins and Macs) are the world's best in point of flavour.

McINTOSH APPLES IN NIAGARA COUNTY, NEW YORK

In New York State, Mohawk Valley farmers found good profits in shipping fruit to New York City. Pennsylvania farmers had Philadelphia as a great fruit consuming market. Cargoes of apples were sent overseas, even as far away as India. They brought wonderful prices abroad. By 1850 Ohio had become interested in fruit; and by 1860 Michigan apples joined Ohio fruit in eastern markets.

Although Cape Cod was first to market its native cranberry and has maintained world leadership, Michigan as early as 1840 also started harvesting the red rubies; and in 1843 shipped 2,000 barrels east.[5]

Peaches never really succeeded in the Northeast. Gradually they worked their way to the South until, as at the present time, Georgia and her sister States captured most of the commercial production of this fruit. However, around 1830-50, Long Island, Delaware, and Maryland stood pre-eminent in peach production. For example, in 1847, the State of Delaware alone shipped 300,000 baskets to market.[6]

Grapes, during this period, flourished in New England, particularly in Connecticut. Massachusetts was also interested in their culture, as is shown by the origination of the famous Concord grape at Concord, Massachusetts, by Ephriam Bull.

Most of the Northeast and much of the old Northwest Territory was rich in native wild grapes. Although good for jelly, they were worthless for table use and for wine. For this reason, from early times, farmers interested in making wine began importing types of wine grapes from France, Spain, and Italy. By 1840 a section of New York State and parts of Ohio, Kentucky, and Illinois attempted

to establish an American wine industry. Their attempts met with mixed failure and success.

Among the early leaders in vineyard development was Nicholas Longworth who, in Ohio, produced an excellent wine from Catawba grapes. The extent of the industry by 1853 is shown by the fact that the Ohio-Kentucky and the Illinois-Indiana grape regions had 2,500 acres planted to grapes.[7]

California (outstanding in grape culture today) as early as 1849 led all the nation in wine production—58,-000 gallons.[8] Through the Civil War, Ohio recaptured the leadership in wine—in 1859 producing 586,000 gallons of the 1,618,000 gallons made in America.[9] Kentucky that year produced 179,000 gallons; Indiana, 102,900 gallons; and the rest came from New York and North Carolina.

Thus, by 1860, apple, pear, and peach orchards were fairly well-established in sections of America suitable to each. A market for fruit was beginning to develop, but even so, standards of quality and amounts of production were still but shadows of what lay ahead. The citrus industry of Florida, Texas, and California; the raisin and prune business of California; and the pineapple production of Hawaii awaited three things—the tin can, rapid transportation, and scientific breeding and culture.

Some mention may be made here, out of proper sequence, of the extent of recent scientific development. The growth of sprays and dusts for combating insects and blights, the modern packing and distribution systems—are of late development. But even before the Civil War, scientific breeding had begun.

For example, the farmers in the old Northwest Territory soon found that they needed hardier apples than those

they had brought with them from New England and New York. So, to develop cold-resistant varieties, Russian apples were introduced and crossed with native stock. Men like J. L. Budd of Iowa and C. Gibb and W. Saunders of Canada devoted themselves to this work. Also, Government experiment stations, particularly those in Iowa, Minnesota, South Dakota, and New Hampshire, somewhat later advanced the breeding. So, too, did the Central Experiment Farms at Ottawa, Canada.

The Russian apples do resist cold, but they are poor keepers and not good eating. In combination with American varieties, however, hardy fruit of high quality was obtained. Some of the more famous Russian-American crosses are Duchess, Wealthy, and Patton Greening.

The extent of the work being done in apple breeding alone is attested by the fact that at the New York Experiment Station nearly 10,000 seedlings have been grown, and some three dozen of these have been found worthy of commercial production. A few are Courtland, Milton, Lodi, Macoun, and Early McIntosh.[10]

[1] Benson, A. E. *History of Mass. Horticultural Society,* Boston. 1929
[2,3] Talbert, T. J. and Murneek, A. E. *Fruit Culture.* Philadelphia. 1939
[4] Report of the Secretary, Mass. Board of Agriculture. Boston. 1838
[5] Annual Report, 1843. United States Patent Office
[6] Annual Report, 1847. United States Patent Office.
[7] Annual Report, 1853. United States Patent Office
[8] United States Census. Agriculture. 1850
[9] United States Census. Agriculture. 1860
[10] Talbert and Murneek. *Op. cit.*

CHAPTER XIV

EXIT THE MAN WITH THE HOE

"Bowed by the weight of centuries he leans
Upon his hoe and gazes on the ground,
The emptiness of ages in his face,
And on his back the burden of the world.
Who made him dead to rapture and despair,
A thing that grieves not and that never hopes,
Stolid and stunned, a brother to the ox?"
—Edwin Markham

MARKHAM'S lines in "The Man With the Hoe" paint a distressing image of the peasant, but these lines were not true of the American farmer in 1899, when they were written. They were a picture of what had been true, of course, in Europe.

Actually, Markham used as his image the familiar painting of Millet's, and he did not limit his protest against social conditions to agriculture. As Untermeyer says, ". . . in the figure of one man with a hoe, he drew a picture of men in the mines, men in the sweatshop, men working without joy, without hope . . . it caught up . . . the passion for social justice that was waiting to be intensified in poetry . . ." [1]

Agriculture is laborious, and the man with the hoe does exemplify farming as a part of the history of mankind. But in America, once the frontier period of colonial ag-

174

riculture had passed, labor was lightened. It was a progressive process, and it still goes on, as farming becomes more and more mechanized and efficient. The symbolical man with the hoe was shown the exit from the farms of this country in the period of the Great Expansion, between 1784 and 1861, when mechanization began to replace human muscles with those of animals pulling the first real farm machines.

The process is, of course, more than the mere invention, development, and utilization of machines. It is part and parcel of the spirit of progress which is typically American. When this period in farm history began, nine out of ten persons in the United States lived on and by the soil. By the time this period ended, production had so tremendously increased by means of better farming that we were well on the way toward our present status. Today, with less than a third of our people farmers, we produce stupendous quantities of food.

The story of the farmer providing himself with machines divides itself into two periods. First, there is the development of machines which were operated by animals. This period ended roughly at about the time of the Civil War. Second, from that time to and through the present, there is the replacement of animal muscle by motors—electric, gasoline, and Diesel.

Probably the epitome of the whole business is the combine-reaper. This one machine displaced the older reapers, binders, and threshers, as well as the pioneer farmers with their sickles and cradles. A modern mastodon, replacing 170 unskilled men and 145 skilled workers, with a single engineer at the helm, it does the work of 315 men! [2]

Early Machines

Behind the combine is a long story of Yankee inventiveness. To go back to the post-Revolutionary period, farmers had exchanged the narrow circumstances and the thinner soil of much of the eastern seaboard for the more fertile prairies. Cotton had become important because of the cotton gin, but, in the main, most agriculture was still wretchedly conditioned.

It is difficult to realize the fact, but mechanization is hardly a century old. Farmers are still to be found who have worked through the transition from Biblical-style tools to tractors. There were many farms, particularly those back in the by-passed hilly regions and those along the frontier, where the old colonial methods were long in use. Plows, great and massive wooden contraptions, were so ineffective that fields were commonly plowed, not once, but two or three times, to break open the soil.

Harrows were brought into use early enough in the nineteenth century, but they were no more than wooden frames studded with jagged scraps of iron. These scratched the ploughed soil but did little towards breaking up the clods and sods.

Sowing and planting were even more primitive. Cereals were broadcast by hand, as they had been long ago in ancient Egypt. Farmers even sowed some hardy things like clover on top of the final spring snow. Corn, like most larger seeds, was planted by hand. After the harrow had gone over it, the field was hilled; and then holes were made by a spade thrust. The corn was tossed in, the spade was withdrawn, and the hole was closed over by trampling the spot.

Hay was cut with a scythe, raked with great wooden

rakes, and then tedded and gathered by a fork. Corn was cut with a knife, piled into sheaves, and left to dry. Grains were reaped by the Biblical sickle until about 1800, when there appeared the cradle, an importation from Europe.

The Cradle

The cradle, one of the first improvements in the harvesting of grain, was a very simple tool. The ancient sickle was a curved blade of steel with a keen edge along its inner surface. The strongest sickles were made from swords, for sword steel was of the best and would take and hold an edge. With a sickle a good man might cut an acre of grain in a day—for men worked long hours then, from dawn to dark.

The cradle was a device which added a tier of three or four similarly curved wooden fingers above the sickle blade. It had the value of holding the grain against the knife-edge of the sickle and of gathering the cut grain into bundles—a fact which made subsequent gathering and tying into sheaves much easier.

The Plow

It was the modern plow, coming to the fore in this period, which really opened the great age of farm development. This age, concluding at about 1860, is considered as being without equal in history.[3] Historians like to write of the "agricultural revolution" as meaning a later time of political and social turbulence. The real revolution was mechanization, for it first freed mankind from the back-breaking labor which had been its lot since the beginning of time.

The first improvement of the plow in America came when odd scraps of steel or iron were fastened upon the hardwood, home-made tool, preventing the wood from being splintered or broken upon rocks, and preventing rapid wear. But since they also made it impossible for the plow to "scour" itself, the old horseshoes, sawblades, and hoeblades often made the work of plowing somewhat more difficult.

At least one team of oxen was required to draw these plows. Usually one man rode the plow to keep it biting, a second man led the oxen, while a third and sometimes a fourth followed behind with hoes to break up the larger clods and to open spots the plow had skipped. All these plows did was to stir up the soil. With them, it was impossible to turn the soil over so that the top sod and litter would be buried and the fresh undersoil brought to the surface.

On the continent and in England, the old system of cereal farming was gradually being transformed into the mixed type of farming—a slow and difficult business because of inherited feudal conditions. There, too, improved tools (especially plows) were being developed.

In America, an imported European plow called the Rotherham was distinguished by an efficient mouldboard. Previously, mouldboards had been made to suit the whim of the individual. No one had studied the function of that portion of the tool.

Then, in 1797, Charles Newbold of Burlington, New Jersey, took a step forward. Following the Rotherham model, he cast his plow in iron. It was a plough which needed only one man to operate it and which really did turn the soil completely over. Newbold spent his fortune

of some $30,000 in an attempt to popularize his invention but spent it vainly.[4] Farmers watched his demonstrations in amazement.

"It seems to do a good job," some said, doubtfully.

"Aye, just look at the way it turns that virgin sod over!" a few volunteered.

"But," objected most of them, "it's made of iron—and iron will poison the soil!"

And that was the fate of the Newbold plow. The farmers refused to touch it for fear of ruining their land.[5] Old superstitions were even more difficult to uproot than the prairie sod.

Soon other inventors in America began to improve the plow. David Peacock, also of Burlington, New Jersey, was given a patent in 1807 for a plow with a cast-iron mouldboard and a wrought-iron share.[6] Finally there was Jethro Wood, a New York Quaker. He did not invent the modern plow but improved upon previous ideas. His great service was in selling the idea of a metal plow to the farmers.

It is related [7] that as a boy he melted down some of the household pewter to cast a small plow. This he hitched to the family cat, using reins cut from his father's driving harness. In 1812 he cast a toy iron plow, using a potato carved to shape as a pattern. By 1819 he had perfected his plow and won a patent. In a few years, he so popularized it among farmers that scores of manufacturers all over the East pirated his design.

Daniel Webster, the great Yankee statesman, interested himself in the case and obtained some justice for Wood, who in the meantime had distinguished himself by designing and making cast-iron stoves. By the time of his

death in 1834 Wood was heavy with honors, although probably still poor in money.

The improvements that Wood developed, aside from his success in overcoming the prejudice of farmers against a metal plow, were two. First, his plow was so designed that each square inch of surface bore wear equally and thus wore out uniformly, without any weak spots. Second, he cast his plow in several, interlocking parts instead of in a single unit. Thus, if one section of his plow broke while in use, that section could be replaced at slight cost.

By this time the farmers were struggling with the task of breaking the prairie sod.

"First the plow does nothing more than dig a shallow ditch," a farmer said, "as if a stick had been dragged along; or else the plow snags in a clump of deep grass roots and then skips out of the ground entirely."

"The iron is too soft," said another farmer. The cutting edge dulls so quickly that it can't shear through the elastic grass roots. And the heavy soil plasters itself against the plow iron, and won't scour off."

Thus the next step in the development of the plow was necessary. This was the use of steel in place of cast iron.

John Lane, a Lockport, Illinois blacksmith, is usually given the credit for the development. He made a wooden plow and sheathed its cutting edge and wearing surfaces with strips cut from old saws. The plows were an instant success and were probably the first that successfully turned the Illinois prairie loam. Lane did not seek a patent, and soon his steel plows were widely copied.

Lane's plow came out in 1833. John Deere and Leonard Andrus of Grand Detour, Illinois, presented their steel plows to the public in 1837.

The story of what each man contributed to the development of the steel plow is very much of a controversy. In 1846 Deere sold his interests to Andrus and moved to Moline, where he organized Deere & Company. The holdings of Andrus eventually passed to the present J. I. Case Company of Racine, Wisconsin. In 1937 these rival companies staged separate celebrations at Grand Detour; one emphasized Deere, and the other, Andrus.

Deere, instead of using a wooden base upon which small pieces of steel were mounted, boldly took the largest saw he could find—one made for a sawmill. Using a wooden form for an anvil, he hammered the saw to shape against the wood.

His share and mouldboard were thus a single piece. The coulter was omitted. The steel tool was fastened to an oaken frame, which also served as the landside. Being thus simple, the plow was light in weight. Deere, a giant of a man, carried the plow on his back to the field where he gave its first demonstration.[8] The new steel plow was a quick success. Deere is credited with making the plowing of the prairies possible.

Other inventors soon followed Deere's lead. William Morrison brought out a new kind of steel for plows in 1868. He welded a sheet of heavy soft iron between two thin plates of steel, the first compound plate ever made. For once, agriculture led the way for Mars.[9]

Another inventor, James Oliver, a Scotchman living at South Bend, Indiana, saw his big chance in 1855. Working as a moulder, he discovered his foundryman employer was on the verge of bankruptcy. The iron plows being made were a drug on the market; so Oliver, for $88.96, purchased a quarter interest in the business.[10]

He had the idea that iron plows could be made satisfactory if the metal went through the tempering process known as chilling. This made the iron sufficiently hard, but also made it brittle. For twelve years he labored; and in 1867 he finally worked out a method which hardened the surfaces of the castings but left the interiors soft and pliable. Thus the chilled steel plow came into being, and Oliver won wealth and fame.

With Oliver's work the radical development of the plow as a basic tool was complete. Much remained to be done, but further improvements were in reality mere refinements. Even so, plow-making in America before 1860 had become a big business. By 1845, in Massachusetts alone there were seventy-three plow manufacturers turning out 61,334 plows annually, plus other tools. By 1855 Massachusetts was making 152,688 plows each year.[11] Pittsburgh was another center for plow production; and so were Chicago, South Bend, and Moline. At the Moline plant alone, in 1858, John Deere was making 13,000 plows a year.[12]

Other Tools

During this time most other farm tools were also being improved and developed. The grass cutter or mowing-machine, replacing the scythe, was one of these. It emerged by 1840; and by 1856, when the Buckeye mower appeared, the haymaker as we know it today was essentially complete.

The horse-drawn hayrake was another contrivance which, although simple, was long in being perfected. Raking hay, along with tedding, had been since time immemorial the province of boys. But boys were often

scarce; and so the hayrake drawn by a horse was soon attempted. The first rakes were the familiar two-wheeled carts with a row of wooden slats hung from the axle. With them "a boy with a horse could do the work of five or six with hand rakes." [13]

Forward-pointing teeth were fastened to the bottoms of the slats so that they just cleared the ground. The spring action of the slats enabled the teeth to rise over stones and inequalities in the ground. A lever lifted the teeth when the rake was filled or when the rake reached the line of windrows waiting for the wagon. Steel-spring, horse-drawn rakes appeared just as soon as steel of proper temper and price was available.

Threshers, now units in the great combines, were developed as independent and portable units. One early type was the "ground hog." It was a spiked cylinder whirled inside a box. The power was supplied by a horse traveling around at the end of a beam attached to a system of gears which multiplied the rotary motion. The threshed grain was winnowed by a blast from a hand-operated fan. By 1840 these "ground hogs" were in common use.

H. A. Pitt of Winthrop, Maine, developed a huge thresher in that year of 1840. Powered by a horse treadmill, the grain was threshed by being drawn through a series of rollers and beaters. The cleaned seed, ready for market, dropped out of a pipe at one end of the contraption, while the straw and chaff were collected conveniently at other points.

By 1860 these threshers, modified by experience, were in comparatively large supply. Privately owned, they toured the grain-growing States on previously arranged schedules, visiting each farmer in turn and threshing his

grain. This emancipation from the flail was a great step forward.

Planters

Machines to plant seeds were eagerly desired because hand planting was slow, irregular, and expensive. Machines for reaping are efficient only with even stands of grain; and hand sowing inevitably resulted in uneven planting.

One Eliakin Spooner was given a patent for a grain drill in 1799. It was not until 1840 that planters were successful enough for general use by farmers. That year, John Gibbons of Adrian, Michigan, patented a grain drill which regulated the amount of seed deposited. That elementary drill was followed two years later by another, invented by Moses and Samuel Pennock of Chester County, Pennsylvania.[14] This drill sowed seven rows at a time, spacing them on nine-inch centers and covering the seed. Drawn by two horses, the machine could plant from ten to fifteen acres a day.[15]

Before long, improvements were made—and improvements have continued to be made. It is now possible to drill twenty rows at a time; to open and to close the furrows; to plant exact amounts of seed; and to scatter precise amounts of fertilizer over some 50 to 200 acres a day, depending upon the power available and the size of the machine, as well as upon the character of the soil.

Corn planters were similarly developed between 1840 and 1860. They were, at first, single horse-drawn boxes mounted on plowlike frames. In front there was a little plow which opened the furrow. A device dropped corn at proper intervals as the machine rolled along. In the

Cutting Grain on a Minnesota Farm

rear were fingers and another wheel which closed and rolled the furrow. With these machines corn could be planted on six to ten acres a day.[16] In contrast, the man with a hoe would be hard driven to plant a half acre of corn in a day.

Cultivators also appeared during this twenty-year period. The first cultivators were V-shaped frames with teeth so arranged that they hoed five rows at a time. Thus one man could cultivate five rows (as rapidly as he could persuade his horse to move), and a great deal of time and human energy was saved.

Harrows were similarly developed. The great wooden frames were laid aside, and light steel frames armed with sharp teeth appeared. These pulverized the soil much better and much more rapidly than had been possible before, and needed but one horse instead of two plodding oxen.

Small tools were also greatly improved during this time. They were now made of high quality steel. Being lighter and sharper, they made handwork easier.

All in all, by 1860 the farmer's lot was vastly improved. We can imagine him saying to his father: "I can do as much work with one horse as you could, when you were my age, with several teams of oxen and half a dozen men. And I can do it better, and make more money, too."

The Reaper

To conclude this chapter on the replacement of human strength by animal muscle, there remains mention of the most important machine of all, the reaper. Considering the time and labor expended, cereals for ages had been the least profitable crop. Therefore, in much of the old world,

mixed farming came to replace the old fashion of growing mainly wheat.

Like most basic inventions, the reaper was the brain-work of many men, both abroad and in America. Two men, Americans both, however, are usually considered to have developed the first practical reapers. They were Cyrus H. McCormick and Obed Hussey. Today it is the McCormick reaper which is important. Under the sponsorship of the International Harvester Company, a massive corporation, it enjoys world-wide popularity.

The question of which man invented which parts is confused. Some facts, however, are known: Hussey obtained a patent for his reaper in 1833 and made a public demonstration at Cincinnati on July 2, 1833.[17] McCormick gave his public demonstration in July of 1831 but did not obtain a patent until 1834—and then did so very much against his will.

The story is that McCormick, not satisfied with his machine, hoped to improve it before taking out a patent; but he finally applied for a patent when he saw a picture of Hussey's machine in 1833.[18]

Hussey was a Nantucket Yankee ex-sailor who appeared in Cincinnati about 1830. A friend challenged him to invent a reaper. Hussey had no experience as a farmer; but with Yankee audacity he turned out a working reaper, got his patent, and had his machines at work, all within a year's time.

His reaper was a heavy, strong cart mounted on two wheels and drawn by two horses in tandem. The wheels turned a gear train, which caused a knife to slide back and forth along the forward edge of a platform extending to the right of the cart. This knife ". . . consisted of a

series of triangular plates riveted to a flat iron bar" and moving beneath slotted tufting fingers.[19]

·In operation, the knife sheared off the grain as the horses pulled the cart into it. The stems collected on the platform until they were raked off by a man who walked beside the machine. Other men followed behind the cart and gathered the grain into carts, so that the ground would be clear for the reaper on its return trip. This reaper could cut from twelve to fifteen acres a day with the small model, and fifteen to twenty with the larger one.[20] Its important features were the cutter bar with the notched knives and the slotted tufting fingers. They are retained in the reaper of today.[21]

Hussey was a great inventor but a poor business man. His machine was not properly merchandised, and gradually the public lost interest in it. In 1858 he sold out to William F. Ketchum for $200,000. Ketchum, a leader in mowing-machine development, also had a career as a reaper manufacturer.[22]

Cyrus Hall McCormick was of Scotch descent.[23] He was an altogether different type of man from Obed Hussey. He had "an indomitable will which transcended the stubbornness of his race." As a boy he worked on the family farm at Walnut Grove, Virginia, between periods of schooling. When only fifteen he made himself a lighter cradle to ease his labor in the farm's grain fields; and when eighteen, he made himself a set of surveying instruments and invented a hillside plow of much merit.

His father, Robert McCormick, had long been working on the invention of a reaper but without success. His final model, in 1831, destroyed more grain than it harvested. Doubtless Cyrus helped his father on this invention and thus became familiar with the problems involved. In 1831 Cyrus McCormick went to work on a reaper of his own.

"This first machine . . . had a straight-edged reciprocating knife, actuated by gears from the main wheel, a platform extending sidewise (to the right) from the wheel, shafts for a single horse, an outside divider to separate the standing grain from that to be held against the cutter-bar, and fingers to project in front of the blade. The late July machine (a second model) had the improved divider, a better cutter bar provided with saw-toothed incised serrations along its leading edge, and a reel to hold the grain against the knife."

A public demonstration was held on a July day in 1831. The twenty-two-year-old boy, "tall, square-shouldered, high of brow, purposeful, wise before his time, determined, feeling the power of destiny within him," strode behind his machine as it reaped a field of grain near Steele's Tavern, just below the family homestead.

Jo Anderson, a Negro servant who had worked with his master in building the reaper, walked beside the platform, raking the sheared grain into bundles. All about stood farmers, sickles and cradles in hand, interrupted for the moment in the work of cutting that field. They did not realize that they were witnessing the emancipation of grain farmers for all time to come.

McCormick was not satisfied with his machine and settled down to improve it. Hussey's machine in 1833 compelled McCormick to patent his own in 1834; but even so, he did not push production. For example, even by 1840 he had sold but two machines. In 1841 he made none at all, spending a year in correcting faults. In 1842 he sold seven; in 1843, twenty-nine; and in 1844, fifty—these last not only near home, but in New York, Tennessee, Ohio, Indiana, Illinois, Wisconsin, and Missouri. The price was a hundred dollars apiece.

The western orders aroused McCormick's interest; and by 1848 he established himself in Chicago. In partnership with Gray and Warner, cradle manufacturers, he built 500 machines that year; and the next year, forming McCormick, Ogden, & Company, he made and sold 1500 reapers. Personal difficulties developed, and McCormick bought out his partners in 1849 for $65,000. Thus at the age of forty he was established in Chicago as a leading reaper manufacturer. By 1850 he had 120 employees and a factory 190 feet long. In 1851 a fire destroyed his plant, but he rebuilt "bigger and better." By 1859 he had more than 100,000 square feet of production space and 300 men employed.

But production was only one of McCormick's triumphs. He had sales and distribution problems. Each year he put some of his profits into advertising and so became well-known. He sold his machines on the ironclad promise that if not satisfactory, their price would be refunded. Then he added another innovation of easy payments. A farmer need pay down only a third, and then the reaper could pay for itself over a year and a half, with interest at six per cent. McCormick then organized what became a great network of dealer-agent outlets and, accordingly, swept through the market. He not only invented a good reaper, he invented a good business system as well.

Foreign markets interested him, too. In 1849 he sent a machine to the Royal Agricultural Society at London. In 1851, at the Crystal Palace Industrial Exhibition in

London, his reaper, in competition with foreign makes, won the Agricultural Medal, the highest award. So Mc-Cormick steamed into the European market by granting rights to British firms to manufacture his machine. Similarly, he reached into Paris via the International Exhibition of 1855. He sold reapers in Russia as early as 1858; and in Germany and Poland in 1860.

McCormick steadily improved his machine. Chief developments included the self-raking device, which automatically cleared the platform. McCormick was also quick to see the value of the work of other inventors, as in the case of the Marsh canvas belt device. This belt lifted the grain from the platform to an overhead table, where men, stationed there, collected and tied the stems into bundles. McCormick bought the Marsh patent in 1858—as did other manufacturers; for McCormick's was not the only reaper being made.

Thus, by 1860 the reaper had reached dependable development. It was of utmost importance to the North during the Civil War. Secretary of War Stanton said: "The reaper is to the North what slavery is to the South. By taking the place of regiments of young men in the harvest fields, it releases them to do battle for the Union and at the same time keeps up the supply of bread for the nation."[25]

A historian declares: "The entire labor force of the United States probably would have been insufficient to have harvested in season the crops grown that year (1862) by the methods of a generation previous."[26]

The whole picture of what mechanization of the farms meant by 1861 is expressed in the 1860 census:

"By the improved plow, labor equivalent to that of one horse in three is saved. By means of drills, two bushels of seed will go as far as three bushels scattered broadcast, while the yield is increased six to eight bushels per acre; the plants come up in rows and may be tended by horse-hoes . . . the reaping machine is a saving of more than a third in labor . . . the threshing machine is a saving of two thirds on the old hand flail methods . . . The saving in the labor of handling hay in the field and barn by means of horse rakes and horse hayforks is equal to one half . . ."

Thus American agriculture by 1861 had begun its emancipation. Machines had not yet reached even a fraction of their modern importance, but a good beginning had been made. Farmers were producing more with less work than had ever before been the case. The shadow of the man with the hoe had been lifted from the American farm.

[1] Untermeyer, Louis. *Modern American Poetry*. New York. 1919
[2] Hedrick, U. P. *History of Agriculture in New York*. New York. 1930
[3] Bogart, E. L. *Economic History of the American People*. New York. 1935
[4] Faulkner, H. W. *American Economic History*. New York. 1935
[5] Kaempffert, Waldemar. *A Popular History of American Invention*. New York. 1924
[6, 7] Hedrick, U. P. *Op. cit.*
[8, 9, 10] Kaempffert, Waldemar. *Op. cit.*
[11] *Annual Report*. United States Commissioner of Agriculture. 1872
[12] *Country Gentleman*. Philadelphia. October, 1857
[13-17] Bidwell. *Op. cit.*
[18] McCormick, Cyrus. *Century of the Reaper*. Boston. 1931
[19] Miller, M. F. *The Evolution of the Reaping Machine. Bulletin 103*, U. S. Dept. of Agriculture. Washington. 1902
[20] *The Cultivator*. Albany, N. Y. 1844. Quoted by Bidwell. *Op. cit.*
[21] Kaempffert, Waldemar. *Op. cit.*
[22, 23] McCormick. *The Century of the Reaper*. Boston. 1931
Other references to the McCormick reaper are from the book by Cyrus Mc-Cormick previously cited and from material supplied by the International Harvestor Corporation.

PART IV

AGRICULTURE COMES OF AGE, 1861-1929

CHAPTER XV

THE FRONTIER ENDS

BETWEEN the Civil War and the Great Depression which began in 1929, American farming came of age. In the same years, the farmer ceased to be the most important man in the nation.

Listen to Lincoln's words on December 3, 1861: "Agriculture . . . confessedly the largest interest of the nation . . . "[1] And listen to Congress in 1929: ". . . the policy (is) to promote the effective merchandising of agricultural commodities . . . so that the industry of agriculture will be placed on a basis of economic equality with other industries . . ."[2]

Between the two conditions lies a reach of seventy years in which agriculture flourished. The American farmer had had a marvelous opportunity. He had vast resources in land and climates suited to the varied forms of his profession. For a time, it was true, agriculture suffered from the paralysis of magnificent distances. Crops accumulated and rotted many miles from market. But the phenomenal building of the railroads solved that difficulty.

And the farmer had a constantly expanding market. Not only did industry work double in his favor—withdrawing thousands from the fields and creating a hungry city horde—but with our population increasing, mouths to be fed kept pace with mounting farm production.

Yet, in the full flower of maturity, with a continent mastered, with mechanization vastly increasing production
(one man in 1929 could produce almost as much as a hundred men in 1829), and with everything seemingly in his
favor, the farmer fell sick economically, politically, and
socially.

The history of this condition is confused, complicated,
and conflicting. The farmer, submerged and victimized
though he may be by America's industrialization, still remains the basic man. It is the farmer who feeds us all. His
fortune is inextricably woven into the pattern of all national events. Complicated as it is, the farmer's history
can be broken down into various topics which, while not
completely describing his experiences, do serve to high-
light them. The following chapters serve to outline what
happened in these seventy years.

First, because of its fundamental importance, there is
the hard fact that during this period the frontier ended.
To understand the ending of the frontier we need but follow the trend of the land policy of the United States,
which tells the story. The national land policy from its beginnings up to the Civil War has been described in an
earlier chapter.

With the Homestead Act of 1862 our public lands
passed into private hands at an accelerated rate. Between
1860 and 1910 a total of 234,000,000 acres of public lands
became privately owned.[3] In these fifty years the number
of farms increased from 2,044,077 to 6,361,502. In half a
century the number of farms increased three times as
rapidly as they had increased in the two previous centuries
put together.[4]

Today, some public lands remain. Beside the various

national forests, parks, and monuments, we have some 183,000,000 acres.[5] Largely in the Far West, and mostly mountain and desert, this land is hardly suited to farms.

In sharp contrast with this sorry remnant of our once huge common domain, Congress has given away about seventy-five per cent of the areas of our States.[6] Only about a third actually was given or sold to homesteaders for the establishment of farms and homes. About 200,-000,000 acres went for the support of education; about 150,000,000 acres as land grants to railroads; and the rest to various other recipients and to the establishment of national forests and parks.

At first there was land in abundance. The spectacle of the settlements of these free lands is a dramatic and heartwarming story. Immigrants by the millions flocked to America out of the stagnation of the Old World. Of the hardships they suffered, much has been written. Of the trials and triumphs of those desperately hard first years in sod huts on the blizzard-swept prairies, of the bitter lessons of floods and droughts, of insect and bacterial pests and diseases, the same is true. The farmer created wealth for America, not by the usual subservient machinations of trade, but by partnership with Nature.

But there is the dark side of the land policy picture, too —less often related.

Indian Troubles

First, there is the treatment of the Indians. In colonial days in the crowded East, the Indians were deliberately exterminated. In the West, especially beyond the Mississippi, there was room enough for both the Indians and the newcomers at first. But the policy, started in the 1820's,

of moving the Indians of the eastern half of the United
States to lands west of the Mississippi River, disrupted
the Plains Indians. Nevertheless, there were few major
troubles with the Western Indians until about 1860. The
Indians did object to the come-and-go hunters and trappers who invaded their territory; and the more permanent
newcomers lurching westward in covered wagons gave
them even more concern. In many things the Indian was
somewhat naive, but he was far from being the "simple
savage" most modern Americans assume. He could read
the handwriting on the wall almost from the start. Proud,
free, and wide-ranging, he realized well enough that his
days of liberty were numbered.

The Ranchers

Undoubtedly there would have been bloody war between the homesteaders and the tribes eventually, just as
soon as the farmers began really to crowd the Indians.
Actually, it was the ranchers and the miners who caused
the first outbreaks of Indian trouble.

The ranchers, from Civil War days on, flourished between the 95th parallel and the Rockies, from Texas up to
Manitoba. Upon this arid but grass-grown inland empire,
cattle were pastured. Before the Civil War, Eastern farms
supplied most of the market with meat. After the war,
what with rising costs of production in the East and the
fact that the railroads provided cheap transportation from
the West to the markets, the Plains rancher stumbled into
his great opportunity. Until about 1890 the cattle empire
thus created flourished wonderfully. Gradually, farmers
homesteaded the section. Shortly before 1900, the days of
cattle-ranging's expensive exclusiveness ended.

WESTWARD MOVEMENT
Oxen pulled the covered wagons of farmers
migrating to the Great Plains

While it endured, the cattleman's extravaganza was a most colorful period in our agriculture. Roundups, rodeos, drives, stampedes, rustlers, cowboys, range wars— our literature is studded with tales of this great era. The expansion of the rancher began about 1866, when the herds moved up into the grasslands, north from Texas. Subsequently, the ranchers protestingly moved westward, as the flood of homesteaders forded the Mississippi and the farm frontier encroached upon the cattle ranches.

The herds, ranging wild during most of the year, were rounded up each spring, and the ranchers sorted out their beasts by means of the brands burned into their hides. Those selected for market were sent off to the nearest railhead, penned up and fattened, or else shipped into the corn belt for heavy feeding. When fat enough, they were again loaded onto cattle cars and rushed to the packing houses at such centers as Chicago, St. Louis, and Omaha.

These railheads, known as "cattle towns," were wide-open, fast-growing communities built up by cattlemen and cowboys. Dodge City, Kansas, on the Santa Fe trail, was one of the most famous. Others as robustly colorful were Miles City, Montana, and Ogallala, Nebraska.

On the range itself life was vigorous and crude. The old law of force, modernized by the Colt revolver, sometimes held sway. The ranchers, some of whom were almost feudal barons, ruled their men vigorously and also organized themselves, not only to eradicate "rustlers" who stole their cattle, but also to present a united front in support of their activities, some of which were actually illegal.

One such illegal activity was the fencing of the range. Waterholes in that dry land were precious, and the rancher who fenced in a waterhole with his land pre-

vented less fortunate ranchers from doing business. He kept his fences intact by means of his "pistol-packing" cowboys.

Of course this enclosing of land was not legal. But the extent of the practice can be judged from the fact that by 1888 at least 8,000,000 acres of range land, supposedly common property, were fenced in.[7] The practice was widespread, and fanufacturers of barbed wire did such a volume of business that by 1874 they reduced the price of their product to twenty cents a pound.[8]

The cattle barons fought each other over this enclosing. Only by submerging of their interests to the purposes of compromise was open war averted. The associations were vital in their strong but futile effort to keep homesteading farmers away from the waterholes and the more fertile acres.

"This will be the end of most of the great ranches," was the bitter complaint of the cattlemen. "Soon the whole western country will be a mass of fenced-in farms, and there won't be room for big herds of cattle. And anyhow, the farmers plow up the grass."

Even more important to the ending of the ranching era was the outbreak of various cattle diseases, such as Texas fever and "foot-and-mouth" trouble. State after State passed quarantine laws against moving cattle from other States into their territory. Thus, legally enough, the end of the free range was hastened.

Upon the Indians, the effect of the expansion of ranching was immediate and bloody. Cattle needed vast reaches of land which had always been the Indians' hunting ground. The ranchers simply pushed the Indians out of their way, slaughtering them as quickly as possible. The

Indians were doomed; but they fought back furiously enough for a time to maintain their rights.

The Miners

The miners were not, at first, a menace to the Indians, being few and far between; although Indians occasionally did murder careless prospectors in the mountains. However, when gold was discovered in California and the '49 gold rush began, it was a different story. The subsequent discovery of gold, copper, and silver in other States increased the influx of miners. As a result, miners swarmed all over the West. In fact, they led the way for both the ranchers and the homesteaders.

California had its first rush in 1849. Colorado had its great rush in 1859. Other great discoveries in Colorado, such as that along the Platte, the one near Boulder, that near Denver, and those near Leadville, brought such hosts of people into the Territory of Jefferson (as it was called in 1859) that the section became the Territory of Colorado in 1861 and the State of Colorado in 1876. There was no more room in Colorado for the Indians after the miners arrived. And what happened in Colorado was duplicated more or less in all the other territories in the Far West.

All through the Rockies and the Sierras, mining towns multiplied in a grand and glorious boom. The famous Comstock Lode was only one such discovery, although in the thirty years before 1890 it produced something like $340,000,000.[9] The hills and valleys and even the deserts brimmed with picturesque life.

The Indians objected to this overrunning of their home-

lands. Actually, much of the area had been set aside forever for them by the Great Father in Washington. But the white man wanted it now and he took it. Indians were pushed aside by the miners, slaughtered by the ranchers, and exiled by the homesteaders. But these Western Indians were not like the smaller and weaker tribes of the East. They were a strong and comparatively numerous people. Accordingly, trouble developed into actual war, in which the United States Army itself finally entered.

This era of Indian Wars may be thought of as beginning with the Sioux outbreak in 1862, bloody trouble which was closely followed by the bitter "revolt" of the Cheyennes and other tribes. The climax of Indian warfare came in 1876. Following the famous "massacre" of United States Army troops under General George A. Custer, the Army finally defeated the Sioux and their great chief, Sitting Bull.

The whole picture of the Indian Wars is a horrible one. There was, for example, that episode in August of 1862 when the Sioux killed a large number of white men and women in Minnesota in a few days. Some historians place the number at 490, others at 737. In return the Indians suffered a grim reprisal—punishment which included hanging thirty-eight braves on one gallows.[10] There was the day in 1864 when Colorado settlers, 1,000 strong, surprised a large number of the Cheyenne tribe of Black Kettle on the Sand River and slaughtered about five hundred of them, mostly women and children.

Whites scalped Indians exactly as the Indians did the whites. Here is a single description of our own methods of fighting the Indians: "The men used their knives, ripped open women, clubbed little children, knocked them on

the heads with their guns, beat their brains out, mutilated their bodies in every sense of the word." [11]

With gold and silver to be mined, with cattle to be grazed, with farms to be established—and a great economic and social pressure pushing men and women ever westward from the East—the white pioneers were determined to take the land. The original Americans had to be destroyed. That they objected was only natural. The cost in blood and horror may not be reckoned. But the price, unquestionably high as it is, can be charged against the onward march of civilization. In a sense, the Indian Wars were one result of our national land policy.

Immigration

The second effect of our land policy was the stimulation of immigration. The opportunity offered by the Homestead Act immediately created a vast movement westward from the East and even from the still sparsely settled region of the Mississippi valley. The social and economic effects were profound, not only in the communities which the migrators abandoned, but also in those which they established.

Considering our national life as a whole, the stimulation of immigration from abroad was of even greater importance.

"Free land!"—Those two magic words once again were on every tongue in a dozen countries of the Old World.

The response was stupendous. In the twenty years from 1860 to 1880 alone some 5,500,000 persons came to the United States seeking wider opportunities. And the significant thing about this is that most of those who mi-

grated were or became farmers. Later migration, sharply different in its Southern European and Near East origin, was urban in character. These later immigrants bulged out the slums of our cities and our industrial towns.

In those decades after the Civil War, the farmers who came were poor, ambitious, and energetic. They swarmed over the seas, on across America and, once on the land, dug in. Somehow, they endured the first winter, often in a sod hut or a log cabin. Then followed years of bitter labor—but labor lightened by progress and prosperity, and labor sweetened by liberty. Gradually, even within the lifetime of the elders of the immigrant families, these hard-working farmers became solid and substantial citizens. They were not native-born, but they were Americans, a vital part of our nation.

Broadly speaking, in contrast with the British character of early days, the first waves of settlers brought here by the Homestead Act were Germanic. They sprinkled themselves very generally about the Middle West, with some concentration in Wisconsin and some in Texas. Scandinavians came in numbers a little later.

At first, the Southern States, such as Texas, Oklahoma, and Arkansas, were settled from the Old South; while Kansas and Nebraska were settled from New England and New York. This native migration continued to flow on due west into the emptiness beyond, but the native-born migrants were soon joined by immigrants from the British Isles, Germany, and Scandinavia.

This immigration of farmers and ranchers of North European origin continued until about 1890. In its place came the tidal wave of people from Southern Europe, Eastern Europe, and the Near East. Since this latter phase

of immigration, which continued until the restrictive policy was finally enforced, was not agricultural, our public land policy had little to do with their coming. But, between 1860 and 1880 particularly, it was the Homestead Act with its "Free Land!" that brought here so many able, industrious, and valuable farmers.

Such a tremendous migration and development was not, of course, conducted without abuses. Steamship and railroad companies often resorted to devious methods in their cashing in on the business. The shipping organizations were chiefly British, for after the Civil War, America abandoned her merchant marine and turned her back on the sea. These shipping companies packed their vessels so tightly with humanity that traveling conditions were almost inhuman. Legitimate agents toured Britain, Germany, and Scandinavia. Others were not too scrupulous in selling tickets to trusting immigrants, tickets for ships and lines that did not exist. Similarly other rascals, pointing out that many immigrants would be too late to obtain the best free land, sold titles on impressive parchments to established farms or to land. When the immigrant arrived, he found his lands existed, perhaps—but only on the top of a mountain or under the waters of a river. If a farm had been purchased, sometimes it did actually exist —but its real owners were busy cultivating it.

The American railroads, on the other hand, did very well by the immigrant farmers. Congress had given the various western railroads grants of something like 1,000,-000 acres. The idea was to give the projected roads a physical asset as a sort of security to use in coaxing money out of the pockets of reluctant investors so that the roads might be built. With the roads built, the value of all land

was so greatly increased that both the roads and the people (the Government) profited.

So, once the roads were built, the railroads rushed to cash in on their land grants. By every device known to the art of propaganda of the day, the roads encouraged settlers to come. They scoured the Eastern United States for prospects, and they invaded Europe with their publicity.

Very generally, the job was done honestly enough. There were episodes of trickery, of course, but the roads, steering migration to their own advantage as they did, helped make the development of the West rapid and prosperous. Wherever the steel rails reached, farmers followed, towns sprang up, loads of manufactured materials flowed westward—and farm produce came back.

Probably the greatest abuse out of the tidal wave of migration that swept westward until the frontier was ended, was committed by Americans themselves. Faults existed in the legislation; and while remedial measures were passed, it was usually the case of locking the barn door after the horse was stolen. For example, a timber company might have scores of its employees ostensibly homestead a forested region. Then, in due time, these "homesteaders" turned over their holdings for a small consideration to the company. Similarly, a mining company eventually could gain ownership of an entire field of mining land.

When such chicanery became a flagrant abuse and public clamors against it arose, Congress consented to investigate in 1879. A commission was appointed—but the reforms it suggested were ignored. Actually, it was not until conservationists became strong enough numerically and articulate enough politically to have weight in Con-

gress that anything to remedy the situation was seriously considered. No important remedies were placed in effect until almost anything of any value had been given away or already taken.

It is possible both to praise and to blame the Homestead Act. As the ultimate expression of our fumbling land policy, it did bring about the settling and development of the West. It made possible a multitude of farms, and this stabilized the Government certainly much more than the ranchers and the miners would have done. But we beggared our nation, so far as providing for the future goes. We have nothing left of what was once a tremendous asset. Formerly, when depressions came, some of the population moved to the West. In a sense, the frontier was the nation's capital.

We have squandered it—and now there is nothing left for emergencies. We cannot grow any larger, physically.

[1] Lincoln's First Message to Congress.
[2] Act of Congress creating the Federal Farm Board.
[3] Edward, E. E. *Lincoln and Agriculture.* Washington. November, 1937
[4] Bogart, E. L. *Economic History of the American People.* New York. 1935
[5] Gras, N. S. B. *A History of Agriculture.* New York. 1935
[6] Rose, Earle D. *Squandering Our Public Land. American Scholar,* January, 1933
[7, 8, 9] Faulkner, H. U. *American Economic History.* New York. 1938
[10] Shannon, Fred A. *Economic History.* New York. 1934
[11] Paxson, F. L. *The Last American Frontier.* New York. 1920

CHAPTER XVI

THE TIDE OF DISCONTENT

THE first high light of the 1861-1929 period was the expansion of the farmer into the West and the ending of the frontier. The second was the remarkable situation that, amid all the prosperous development of America in this period, the farmer's lot was not a happy one. The farmer everywhere was affected by two contrary currents during these seventy years.

First there was the powering of farm tools. Then there was the rapid development of Governmental services in support of the farmer, especially the extension of scientific knowledge from the laboratory to the field. Finally, there arrived such modern devices as the automobile, the tractor, the telephone, rural free delivery, and the radio—none of them unmixed blessings, but all helping to end the traditional isolation of the farm.

This development more or less urbanized the farm; but various unhappy conditions emerged, which caused perennial hardship and misfortune for the farmer and his family. Thus at the very hour when American agriculture reached its greatest growth (so far) in our national history, farming also began its comparative eclipse.

Agriculture has suffered because the farmer is no longer the major personage in our national economy. He supports us all, but he has been put into the shadow by

the glitter of Big Business, by the roaring tumult of industry, and by the streamlined carriers of commerce.

This chapter outlines the basic cause of this eclipse and describes something of the response the discontented farmer has made.

Currency

One fundamental root of trouble for the farmer was currency—especially inflated money. This evil appeared at the very beginning of the period, at the time of the Civil War. Since then it has remained a specter which has constantly haunted the nation. The farmer has suffered especially, because he has often been the victim of the vicious cycle caused by his propensity to overproduce. To buy machines, stock, land, and the materials he does not produce himself, he must have money. Since few farmers are or can be capitalists, this has meant that he must often borrow money, with his land as his only security.

To repay the loan with interest, the farmer must produce more. And the more he produces, the less he receives for his corn or wheat or apples, because with every farmer doing about the same thing, the markets are often glutted. And the less he receives for his product, the more, in proportion, he must pay for his machines, his tools, his clothes, and his working capital. The mortgage on his home became the instrument of oppression, and the farmer developed a deep hatred for the banker. He also hated the manufacturer, who produced his tools and machines (and sold them on "easy credit and deferred payments"). Railroads were another devil in the drama, for they took in transportation charges what seemed to the

farmer an unjust share of the price the consumer ultimately paid.

After the Civil War

In general, here is the background of the currency trouble: The years from 1867, when Civil War prosperity ended, to 1897, when a general boom came along, were a period of uncertainty and distress, save for brief spells of good times.

During the Civil War, prices for food soared because of underproduction, since so many young men from the farms were enlisted in service. The Federal Government aided this inflation by running the printing presses overtime to produce greenbacks. Farmers, as a result, overextended by buying more land and equipment. When the war ended, many ex-soldiers, tradesmen, mechanics, clerks —men of varied types of experience and training—obeyed the characteristic desire of Americans for land ownership. They took advantage of the Homestead Act. What they did not realize was that farm prices were very high because of the war boom. They also failed to remember that a boom is often followed by a collapse. And they did not know, as we can see now by looking back, that agriculture had changed and was due for a still greater economic transformation.

Previously it had been a matter of a strong back and a willing spirit. Now, by contrast, agriculture had become capitalistic. Money was necessary. So the new farmers (and many of the old ones) began to borrow.

"All of us newcomers," said one homesteader, "came to the West on borrowed funds; and now we have to borrow to support our families until our farms produce enough."

"We're in debt, too," said others, who had purchased their land outright. "We borrowed money to pay for choicer locations near the railroad. We had to buy them from the railroad companies; and it will take a long time to pay back the loans."

Just so long as prices held, everything was roseate. Then the Federal Government initiated deflation by going back to the gold standard. As money rose, prices fell. The farmer, who had nothing to sell but food and everything else to buy, soon fell behind, as money became "hard" and harder.

Foreclosures

Immediately a host of farmers were unable to meet their mortgage payments. Many even defaulted interest. A wave of foreclosures swept across the country, particularly in the Middle West, where most of the new farms were located. Farmers were compelled to leave the acres upon which they had lavished so much hope and so much labor. They could remain as tenants, or they could go to town and work in shop or factory. Even those who managed somehow to keep a step or two ahead of the sheriff worked harder than ever and received less and less. They came to feel that the bankers, especially those back in the East, where much of the capital to develop the West originated, were sitting in luxury, while the farmers of the West labored vainly.

Railroads

The hate of the farmers for the railroads was widespread. The complaint, of course, concerned the charges which the railroads demanded for carrying. Eastern

farmers were not much disturbed by railroads, but western farmers became very bitter.

The railroads themselves were not in happy condition.
They had been strung along lavishly all over the country. Often, rails were laid in parallel competition with
other lines; some even were built where there was no
possibility of support. So the railroads, too, faced financial
troubles. In an attempt to maintain themselves, they resorted to various expedients.

Industry, powerful and articulate, received many fa-
vors from the roads, but the farmer, solitary and helpless,
was an easy victim for exploitation. The farmer saw his
meagre profits swallowed by what seemed exorbitant
freight rates. He witnessed the railroads demonstrating
loving kindness to big business. What the farmer did not
realize was that the railroads often were poorly managed
and were being very extravagantly milked by big business at the same time.

The farmer can hardly be blamed for his indignation.
We can imagine a Nebraska farmer talking to his neighbor in 1873:

"I got only 30 cents a bushel for my corn and 90 cents
for my wheat," [1] he complained bitterly. "Corn is selling
for 60 cents and wheat for $1.32 back in the East!" [2]

"It's the railroads that are profiting, not us," his neighbor added.

These farmers and their brothers everywhere could
see the roads giving free passes to everyone who had the
least possible legislative influence; see the roads paying
handsome dividends upon watered stock; see them maintaining costly stables of lobbyists wherever they would do
the most good.

"Imagine," a farmer in 1869 might have said, "American railroads are, on the average, forty per cent over-capitalized. We have to pay for that in our rates!"

Then came the spectacle of what can be called the Vulture Era of railroading. Speculators like Jay Gould, Jim Fisk, Daniel Drew, and others made huge personal fortunes out of several of the railroads. Conditions were very bad for the farmer. Although things have long since been bettered, the typical farmer still dislikes the railroads as strongly as he dislikes bankers.

Speculators

Still another element in the farmer's discontent was the greed of the middleman and the irresponsibility of the speculator.

"The middlemen," a farmer could say, "take as much as fifty cents profit out of every dollar paid for the grain we grow.[3] That's much more than we make ourselves!"

The farmer bitterly resented these speculators, who buy and sell farm products without ever so much as seeing the materials they "trade" in. The farmer, the man who gambled on the weather, who endured heat and cold, rain and dust, who labored to exhaustion, could not see why the speculator had any right to harvest where he had not sowed. The farmer thought it wrong that these speculators, by their mysterious machinations, could in a sense determine the price paid the farmer for his produce. The speculator continues today to be a factor in agricultural unrest and one of the causes of great emotional conflict.

The South

The ills bred by currency troubles and by the railroads were effective in proportion to the distance of the farms

to the market. The East was not badly off for this reason. In the South these ills were magnified by the war. There, deflation of prices, costs of transportation, and the high costs of manufactured goods due to the tariff, were all multiplied in effect by general bankruptcy plus the decline in the price of cotton in the world market.

Cheap Money

Thus, all over America, the stage was set for the farmers to do something to help themselves. They had to do something. And they did!

First, there was railroad control, a movement epitomized in the Interstate Commerce Act of 1887. Then there was the Governmental and agricultural organization development of better farming through education and research. The establishment of the United States Department of Agriculture and of various State departments and bureaus of agriculture is a good example. So also is the Hatch Act of 1887.

Finally, there were the various and bitterly fought financial battles, such as the Bland-Allison Act of 1878, the Sherman Silver Purchase Act of 1890, the Federal Reserve Act of 1913, and the Federal Farm Loan Act of 1916. In all these things, agriculture was not the only interest involved. Business, industry, transportation, also were included. But it was the farmer who was most concerned. His influence was exerted particularly in favor of the control of business abuses and especially in pressure for "cheap" money. Many a farmer, struggling with debt and low income, believed that he would be better able to prosper if he had "cheaper" money. So he joined in battle against the intrenched financial power of the East.

The Grange

Of all the farmer's efforts to improve his plight, the Grange was the first significant organization. Its correct name is, of course, the Patrons of Husbandry—but few bother to use the longer title.

The Grange had its beginning in the office of President Johnson. One day in 1866, Lincoln's successor, worried about the farming collapse in the South, ordered the Commissioner of Agriculture to investigate. The Northern mills wanted cotton. The South, for some reason, was not producing enough. So an obscure clerk in the Department of Agriculture, Oliver Hudson Kelley, was sent into Dixie to investigate. What he saw affected him profoundly.

Kelley is not well-known to modern Americans. Boston-born, from a family including such noted ancestors as Dr. Oliver Wendell Holmes and Judge Samuel Sewall, he was much more than a mere clerk. Circumstances had cast him at the moment in that role; but underneath the dignified bearing of this gentleman, already white-bearded at forty years, was the brain and spirit of an original thinker and a fiery crusader. "An engine with too much steam," his friends thought him.[4]

Kelley had left Boston at the age of twenty-three, joining the westward movement of New Englanders to Iowa. Later, he settled at Elk River, Minnesota, as a farmer. He thus gained firsthand an idea of farming and, since he failed at it, a good knowledge of its problems.

Kelley finally entered the Government's service as a clerk in the office of the Commissioner of Agriculture at Washington. His report on conditions in the South was of little importance because, seemingly, it was ignored.

But his personal reactions were very important, because the pitiful poverty of the war-blighted South aroused his latent Puritan zeal. He was afire with a stubborn determination that something had to be done to help the farmer, not only in the South but everywhere in America.

Kelley thought the farmer's plight was much more basic than the temporary economic distress of the day. He felt that farmers were themselves to blame, largely because they were antisocial. To begin with, they were individualists. Unprogressive, suspicious of innovations, chained to inherited customs and habits, they were easy game for all organized and articulate pressure groups.

What the farmer needed, Kelley thought, was a social organization that, compelling a measure of gregariousness, would provide a means of driving home the new ideas, methods, and habits through which improvements could be made. In those days, without newspapers, the telephone, the radio, and without the mail-order catalog, the extension service of the Government, and the 4-H Clubs—to mention a few things—the farmer really was isolated.

Later that year, having left his job, Kelley, back in Boston, mulled over the problem with a niece, Miss Carrie Hall. They concluded that farmers should be organized, and they worked out a plan based on Masonic principles. Frequent gatherings of a social order, made impressive by ritual, would unite the farmers and make possible their education. Miss Hall rendered particular service by insisting that women must be included in the membership. They suffered from isolation even more than did their fathers, husbands, and brothers.

This inclusion of women was a revolutionary idea at

Grangers' Meeting in an Illinois Forest

Sketch by Joseph B. Beale

the time; but Kelley offered no objections. Needing money with which to live, he returned to Washington as a clerk in the Post Office Department. During the summer of 1867 he managed to interest just six of his fellows to join him in establishing the Patrons of Husbandry. They were: W. M. Ireland of the Post Office Department; Reverend A. B. Brosh and William Saunders of the Agricultural Bureau; Reverend John Trimble and J. R. Thompson of the Treasury Department; and F. M. McDowell of Wayne, New York. On the 4th of December, 1867, the National Grange of the Patrons of Husbandry finally came into being. Saunders was master, Thompson lecturer, Kelley secretary, and Ireland treasurer.

Political activity was explicitly banned. Betterment of the farmer was to be accomplished solely through education. With this as his program, Kelley bravely resigned his job and set out to spread the gospel. He had a salary of $2,000 a year—if he could raise it. Fees were set for membership at three dollars for men and fifty cents for women.

Farmers, however, were suspicious, and few would even listen. It was a time of bitter poverty for Kelley; he failed to make even his travel expenses, and certainly not his salary. Often he did not have enough money for postage on his letters home. But his Puritan blood, armored by zeal, was proof against failure.

One Grange was established at Fredonia, New York, the first to be constituted. In Minnesota, by 1870, thirty-seven granges were founded. But that was the whole of Kelley's success.

What the Grange movement needed was a national crisis to dramatize to the farmers their plight. That crisis came. It was the depression which climaxed in the Panic

of 1873. Farmers swarmed into the Grange. Charters could scarcely be written rapidly enough to meet the demand. With farm produce priced suicidally low, the farmers could not find bankers willing to lend money, evn at such exorbitant interest rates as 15 and 20 per cent.[5] Money went into hiding.

Significantly, this wildfire growth of the Grange, a growth which gave it 1,500,000 members,[6] instantly and radically altered its character. Kelley lost control overnight. Education was ignored The new leaders pushed the organization squarely into politics!

Of course, the Grange itself did not officially, as such, go into politics. Instead, its members fathered "outside" political organizations. But Grange members made up these groups, and Grange officers led them. This was true generally in Illinois, Iowa, Minnesota, and Wisconsin, where the Grange was vigorous.

Battling the Railroads

To these wheat and corn States the railroads were obnoxious. The complaints of the farmers rose, loud and angry. Inflamed by anger and suspicion, the farmers, led by the auxiliary Grange organizations, attacked the high and allegedly discriminatory freight rates.

"Wheat sells at fifteen cents a bushel in Iowa, and at a dollar in New York.[7] Is that fair? The high freight rates charged by the railroads are to blame!"

Thus, the so-called Granger Laws came into being in the four above-mentioned States. Legislators, stung into action by Grange pressure, sought to establish uniform and just rates for transportation and for storage—and also to have the rate structure published. These laws were

based upon "the rights of a State to regulate a business that is public in nature although privately owned and managed." [8]

Of course, the railroads fought back. The period was battle-scarred, from the passage of the Illinois Warehouse Act of 1867 and the 1871 Act for fixing maximum rates for transport, down through (and beyond) the establishment of the Interstate Commerce Commission in 1887.

Unfortunately, the various Acts in the States lost immediate effectiveness, because the railroads in general were so near bankruptcy that there was little interest in too strict enforcement. There was, after all, no sense in utterly destroying the railroads. So the battle continued until it became a Federal one, and Federal enforcement was instituted.

The important point however is this: the farmers had won a victory. They had gained class consciousness. They had demonstrated such power that they were no longer helpless victims of the railroads—or of bankers, for that matter.

Greenbacks

Other things, of course, concerned the political organizations of the Grange; but as time passed, the political bias of the Grange proved nearly fatal. The Grange lost its identity in its subsidiary organizations; and, as a unit, the Grange shortly vanished from the political arena. Various political groups were its heirs. One of these was the Greenback Party.

In 1876 the movement for the abolition of banknotes and for the printing of legal-tender paper money by the Government enlisted enthusiastic farmer support. Most

of the Grange members became Greenbackers. Cheap money was always a farmer's dream. Bellowed Solon Chase, Maine publicist: "Inflate the currency, and you raise the price of my steers and at the same time pay off the public debt." [9] (At that time, people really worried about the national debt!)

Greenbackers enlisted support. Only President Grant's veto of the inflation bill in 1877 ended the Party's drive to remake the nation's financial system. The defeat proved fatal to the cheap-money party, and the Greenbackers faded quickly. However, many farmers still regarded cheap money as their only means of salvation. Their determination was reflected in the Allison Silver Act of 1878 and the Sherman Silver Act of 1890. Both of these required the Treasury to purchase each month a specified amount of silver for coinage. In a sense, this was cheaper money.

The background of these acts is this: In 1890, the same depression evils that had boomed the Grange in the Panic of 1873 again came into focus. That year, 60 per cent of Kansas (taxed acreage) was under mortgage—and also 55 per cent of Nebraska and 47 per cent of Iowa.[10] Wheat had averaged $1.50 at New York between 1850 and 1859. Between 1855 and 1899 it averaged only 85 cents. Corn, for the same period fell from 75 cents to 47 cents.[11] In consequence, many farmers refused for years to harvest their crops or to sell them. They burned corn for fuel. They turned hogs into the wheat fields "rather than feed those pigs in Chicago and New York," as many a farmer expressed it.

Thus, when the People's Party appeared, it gathered up the remnants of the political organizations of the Grange

and many farmers who had never before been stimulated to communal activity. In the election of 1892 it won twenty-two votes in the Electoral College.

Merged with the Populists and the Democrats, the movement swept not only the solid South but all save five States west of the Mississippi. Free and unlimited silver coinage, national greenback currency, income taxes, postal savings, Government ownership of all monopolies —such were the ideas supported by the farmers of America behind the party organizations. The silver tongue of William Jennings Bryan fired them almost universally.

However, 1896 initiated a brighter era for the farmers. The great period of overproduction had ended, as the rapid multiplication of the population finally established wider markets. For example, while population in the ten years beginning in 1900 increased by 21 per cent, farm crops, as indexed by cereal production, increased but 1.7 per cent. Thus the farmers had a breathing spell which endured for about a generation. Troubles still existed, but they were not serious until 1920 and again in 1929, when once again the shadows deepened.

Consequently, for the first fifth of the twentieth century, farmers were not too badly off. Still, the old distrust of bankers, big business, railroads, and the rest persisted; and the Farmers' Non-Partisan League, established in 1915 (later the National Non-Partisan League) became a political voice for agriculture that was of great modern importance.

The Modern Grange

Despite its eclipse, caused by political party activities, the real Grange continued to survive and to busy itself

with agrarian problems. One such problem was the effort
to break the grip of the middlemen—the commission merchants. These gentlemen in some instances not only
profited by the sale of farm products, but also, through
the extension of credit to the farmers, gained a strangle-
hold on them.

Co-operatives were the answer the Grangers worked
out. Such organizations were essayed on a nation-wide
basis, although Iowa led the way. There, farmer co-
operatives built their own elevators; and at Des Moines in
1872 the co-operatives financed a central purchasing and
selling agency. In 1873 they started to break the harvesting machine "trust" by making machines for themselves.
In 1874 they made 250 machines and sold them for about
half of the current price. So encouraged, the co-operatives began also to make plows.

So well had Iowa done, that in 1874 the National
Grange invested about $250,000 in farm machine factories
in various sections. In truth, the Grange that year seemed
to have broken the farm machine "trust" and to have
eliminated the middleman—at least so far as showing how
it could be done was concerned. But "Big Business" had
much at stake and fought back bitterly. The "Trusts"
could not face independent competition. Pressure was applied, and in 1875 the Iowa factories failed. Poor manage-
ment was alleged and, if so, doubtless contributed to the
debacle.

Anyhow, to escape debt action, many local Granges
disbanded, and the Granger movement ebbed. The basic
trouble was that the Grange was not sufficiently well-
organized to undertake ambitious programs. Only in a
few places were the farmers actually united, and nowhere

strongly enough to withstand adversity. The National Grange in particular often lacked the full confidence of the local Granges.

The Grange in 1876 needed another Kelley to reorganize it, and there was no Kelley. Then the success of the farmers and other interests in putting railroad regulation under Federal Law took much of the wind out of the sails of the Grange leaders. They could no longer maintain the political faith of their members. Personally and collectively they lacked the fire of a great cause. So by 1880 the Grange no longer had more than 1,500,000 members—it had but 300,000. Its brief day was done—politically.

So, gradually, the Grange returned to Kelley's fundamental principles of education and sociability. As such it has continued, prospering mildly but solidly. It became and has remained a great force for farm betterment. Miraculous in its first growth, unfortunate in its aspiration, through adversity the Grange has recovered its sanity and, now grown to maturity, continues to serve its founding principles.

[1] Shannon, Fred A. *Economic History.* New York. 1934
[2] *Ibid.*
[3] *Ibid.*
[4] Buck, Solon J. *The Agrarian Crusade.* New Haven. 1920
[5] Shannon, *Op. cit.*
[6] Buck, Solon J. *The Granger Movement.* New York. 1913
[7] Shannon. *Op. cit.*
[8] Buck. *Op. cit.*
[9, 10] Bogart. *Op. cit.*
[11] Hibbard, Benjamin H. *History of Public Land Policies.* New York. 1924

CHAPTER XVII

THE RESPONSE OF GOVERNMENT

WHILE the discouraged farmer was trying to improve his unhappy circumstances during this period of seventy years, the Federal and State Governments came to his assistance. In Washington, the United States Department of Agriculture was created; and in every State, departments or bureaus of agriculture were established. Agricultural schools and colleges also appeared.

The United States Department of Agriculture

Among the huge buildings which Washington has reared to house its various businesses, one is occupied by the Department of Agriculture. Its physical bulk, sprawled over acres, dramatizes the staggering responsibilities concentrated inside the white walls.

Boston-born Ben Franklin, father of so many institutions, promoted work that evolved into the Department of Agriculture. In London, just before the Revolution, Franklin collected and sent back to Philadelphia various seeds and plants to interest American farmers. That was actually the germ of the Department, although seed and plant exchange really had begun with Columbus.

Washington continued to import plants; and then when another farmer, Jefferson, became president, the practice was formally organized. Jefferson directed American

consuls to send home seeds and plants. He officially charged the United States Patent Office, then a section of the State Department, to receive and distribute plant material thus received.

For many years this was about all, for farmers, as a class, were not much interested in Governmental aid. But a ferment was working. Like Washington and Jefferson, various other gentlemen farmers and amateur agriculturists interested themselves in the scientific aspects of making things grow better. The interest was particularly keen in the East. In 1827 the Pennsylvania Horticultural Society was established; and in 1829 the Massachusetts Horticultural Society was incorporated. These are but the first two of many such groups.

The Societies stimulated the development of better plants—mostly fruits and flowers—by holding frequent competitive shows. Their members also began to import seeds and plants. It became something of an honor to enter a new pear or apple in a show. These organizations tried to interest ordinary farmers in better methods of culture. The Massachusetts Society, for example, established an experiment station, probably the first "public" station in the United States since the nation was established. New materials were tested, and new ideas of culture were tried and demonstrated. Valuable prizes were offered. Essentially, this was the beginning of the attempt to interest the American farmer, as well as the gardener, in "scientific" raising of crops.

It was not long before this work became so important that the Federal Government expressed interest. In 1839 Congress appropriated a small sum, not merely for collecting and distributing seeds, but also for "prosecuting

agricultural investigations and procuring agricultural statistics."[1] Perhaps unwittingly, the legislators thus created the basic functions of the present Department of Agriculture and established the fact that the welfare of agriculture is a matter of public concern.

Today, the importance of research in farming is recognized. For example, the work of one scientist, Pathologist E. H. Guba at the Waltham (Mass.) Field Station, in developing a new tomato (the "Bay State") puts a million dollars a year into the pockets of greenhouse tomato producers. His new fruit is all but immune to the dreaded mildew that causes vast losses.[2]

All that Congress knew in 1839 was that research was a promising field, one that properly could be financed by the Government for the good of all. So they established the precedent by appropriating a few tax dollars. Thus began one Federal activity which has always been beyond reproach.

Once the snowball was shaped, it grew characteristically. The Patent Office experienced ever-increasing demands for its farming services. It complied with requests of citizens by investigating the culture of sugar cane, the silkworm, soil fertility, the value of legumes for redeeming wornout fields and, most important, the control of insect plagues. In effect, the Patent Office organized a small but active Bureau of Agriculture.

Because of this success, agitation began by 1841 for the establishment of an independent Federal agricultural service. The South opposed any extension of Federal activities; and so, because the North was not enthusiastic, the agitation came to naught. Abolition, secession, and finally the clouds of war sidetracked the issue until 1862.

That year, with the influence of the South removed from Washington, the track was cleared for action. Three great farm bills went through Congress speedily. There was the Homestead Act, previously described, on May 20. There was the First Morrill Act (of which, more later) on July 2. And there was the Act of May 15, which specifically created the Department of Agriculture "for the purpose of acquiring and diffusing among the people of the United States information relating to agriculture in the most general and comprehensive sense, of the word, and to procure, propagate, and distribute among the people new and valuable seeds." [3]

Lincoln, backwoods born, knew something of the farmer's problems. He did much to promote these three bills.[4] He said of the Department: ". . . it will one day realize all the fondest anticipations of its most sanguine friends and become the fruitful source of advantage to all our people . . ." [5]

Once begun, the Department of Agriculture prospered consistently. In general, it has a splendid record. Foreign eyes are often clearer than our own in judging our institutions. Sir Horace Plunkett, Irish agriculturist, in speaking of the Department, says: ". . . perhaps the most popular and respected of the world's great administrative institutions." [6]

The Plant Hunters

Easily outstanding, both in romantic appeal and in service, is the Department's Division of Plant Exploration and Introduction. This work, begun long ago by Franklin's sending home some seeds from London, has placed the farmers of the whole world in its debt. Hardly

a crop is grown anywhere today which has not been improved by American plant hunters. Their work is not
limited to one nation. Plant hunters are scientists, and
they work in co-operation with the scientists of other
countries.

Plant hunting received its big boost in 1870, when a
missionary in Brazil, who enjoyed a big, seedless orange
in the city of Bahia, sent six young trees to the Department of Agriculture. Two of the six were relayed in 1873
to California, where they prospered amazingly.[7] From
those two trees developed California's great orange industry; for that freakish Brazilian orange was the parent
of the navel orange.

Many people knew that the world held similar plants
which would be of great value in various sections of the
United States. We have many climates and many soils.
Nearly every country, from Siberia to Australia, has native plants we can use, as well as plants that can be bred
into our stocks to their improvement. But not much was
accomplished until David Fairchild, a Kansan, persuaded
James Wilson, secretary of the Department in the 1890's,
to organize a corps of explorers. That was the beginning
of the modern office of plant hunters. Fairchild himself
circled the globe time and time again.

One of Fairchild's men was Frank N. Meyer. Before
he was accidentally drowned in crossing a Chinese river,
Meyer spent eleven years wandering in the Asian wilderness. To him we owe such things as the Chinese elm,
flowering cherry trees, hardy roses, blight-resistant pears,
and hardy cabbage. Another Fairchild find was Mark
Carleton, also of Kansas, who discovered in Siberia the
wonderful hard wheats which have so greatly extended

and improved American wheat farming. Another, Wilson Popenoe, is famous for improving the alligator pear, or avocado. He went deep into the Central American wilderness to procure samplings of superior avocado trees.

New Plants

Dramatic in effect have been the successes of new plants introduced in America. For some thirty years the Division ransacked the Saharan oases and the deserts of Arabia and Persia for date palms. Thousands of trees were studied, hundreds of plants were sent home, before the sands of Arizona and California began to produce the fruit.

Then there is tung oil. It is used widely in rapidly drying enamels for automobiles, in making linoleum, and in other such important roles. Formerly, all the tung oil we used (some $20,000,000 worth, as in 1937) came from China and Japan. After 1941 our supply was cut off; but we were for once safeguarded. Beginning in 1904, Dr. Fairchild and his men had brought in superior tung-oil stock, and today the Gulf Coast has many acres covered with tung trees.

Then there is the soybean, probably the miracle plant of tomorrow's agriculture, a source of food, of oil, and of the raw material for plastics. No one today is competent to judge the full value of this one legume. Plant hunters from Washington scoured Manchuria to obtain the best varieties of the soybean. Today, as a result, America has still another new crop—one which in 1940 was valued at $100,000,000.

Old Plants, New Blood

Plant hunters have not only brought in new plants. They have searched the world for new varieties of famil-

iar crops in order to improve our staple crops by "blood transfusions." Some transfusions also help them withstand diseases. Cotton has been improved by new varieties brought from Egypt and from Mexico. One such is the Acala cotton, which produces more to the acre than any other known variety. Rice has been greatly bettered by the upland variety brought from Japan. So great has been our improvement of rice that the Japanese, before 1941, used to send ships to Texas to buy rice, which was better than that raised in Japan.

All in all, there have been some 140,000 items of plant material brought home by this Division of the Department. Every farmer knows about the Russian apples bred into our old stock, of the walnut trees now thriving in California, of the new clovers for the Northeastern States, of the timber bamboo for the tropical areas of Florida, of mangoes in Florida, and so on and on.

Plant Introduction

The mere bringing of a plant or seed into the country is not all. These plants have to be made into citizens. At four stations, in Maryland, Georgia, Florida, and California, new introductions are grown and multiplied under the most rigorous scientific conditions. After being proven to be disease- and insect-free, they are distributed to various agencies, such as the experiment stations operated in the forty-eight States. There they are grown, tested, and, if valuable, bred into native American strains. Only then is the new plant material given to commercial growers for general distribution.

The Division of Plant Exploration and Introduction is composed of a group of highly trained specialists whose

program is far from finished. There are plants to be improved, diseases to be controlled by breeding in resistant strains, and above all, new plants to be tried and tested. This is Governmental service at its very best.

Plant and Animal Breeding

Out of the need for better plants and animals grew the Department's heavy, impressive, improvement programs. The work of plant and animal breeders is highly technical. It depends upon actual rebuilding of plant and animal tissue by means of various techniques used with infinite patience.

From the test tubes and greenhouses of the plant breeder are coming entirely new types of plants. It is one of the most promising fields of science. This subject will be taken up later. It is mentioned here because it was in this (1861-1929) period that a beginning was made in plant breeding—the modern magic which is remaking the plant world. The work of the Department, for example, in searching for what is termed "superior germ plasma" is of basic importance. Through the isolation of such material, the scientist has the elements of creation in his hands and can get to work rebuilding directly, instead of awaiting patiently the whimsies of chance.

Plant breeders in general have been more popularly appreciated than animal breeders, for their work is more immediately valuable to the farmer. The plant breeder has delivered hundreds of new varieties of plants to the farmer—plants that give heavier yields; plants that resist diseases; plants that fruit earlier and so defeat frosts—plants that are really miracles.

The cotton farmer has had new and better varieties

given to him. The potato growers were given such stock
as Kathadin and others. The wheat farmer has received
Turkey, Marquis, Kanred, Ceres, Federation, Tenmar-
que, Ridit, and Oro. New oats have included Iogold,
Iowa, 103, and Markham. The list is nearly endless. In
effect, if anything goes wrong with a crop, the breeders,
like magicians, reach into their laboratories and pull out
a new variety to save the situation.

Rust, smut, and other diseases have been partly conquered by breeding new varieties which shrug off these
troubles. Corn has been increased in size and starch content for field varieties; and sweet corn has been improved
in sweetness and in a shorter growing season. It is possible to breed peas, corn, and other standard vegetables almost as if plants were machines. They can be altered so
that they will be uniform in size and staggered in ripening
time. Canning factories can schedule their program almost to the day. They can construct machines sized exactly
to handle efficiently the vegetables and fruits processed.

Battling Insects and Diseases

Another great field of activity for the Department has
been the waging of war against insects and bacterial diseases. Plant pathology and animal pathology have become
professions.

Most spectacular has been the war against animal diseases. In the sixties and seventies, an epidemic of contagious pleuro-pneumonia among farm animals broke out
and threatened general slaughter. William H. Hatch,
Missouri Congressman, introduced in 1884 his famous
bill that created the Bureau of Animal Industry. Cutting
across State lines and bringing all scientific knowledge of

CATTLE OF TODAY
A twelve-year-old Holstein mother
and her five daughters

the time to bear, the new Bureau stamped out pleuro-pneumonia within five years. More important, the Bureau has prevented the disease from becoming prevalent again.

Thus encouraged, the Bureau struck against hog chol-era, cattle fever, anthrax, and bovine tuberculosis. Now a disease no sooner appears than it is attacked.

The Bureau has not always been successful, but its very existence means that skill and ability are organized for action; that a constant watch is maintained against trouble; while at the same time, programs are maintained against the old stubborn enemies. It is an insurance policy for the many millions of dollars invested in livestock by American farmers.

The fight against insects is less spectacular but of equal importance. The farmer, thanks to the Department, is no longer helpless against the winged hordes that once de-voured fields overnight, even though our annual toll to the pests is still one of our greatest economic losses—war excepted.

Until about 1850, losses through pests and diseases were not of great economic importance. Then, as commerce de-veloped, trouble began. Our native insects and diseases are seldom serious, because, through the years, they are more or less controlled by natural enemies. But against im-ported enemies, our native checks and balances ordinarily are not effective. Enemy alien pests, coming in with the spread of commercial activities and freed of their own controls, spread like wildfire. Significantly, the names of most of our insects and diseases include the adjectives "European," "Dutch," "Japanese," or "Asiatic." Our in-sect troubles were imported, unknowingly, in shipments of various goods.

The first battle against insects came in the late sixties, when the cottony-cushion scale threatened to exterminate the California orchards. The Department organized the Division of Entomology. The entomologists discovered that the natural enemy of the scale is the Vedalia lady-bird, an Australian insect. The bug fighters imported and bred the ladybirds in vast numbers and released them among the orchards. The scale was conquered.

Very soon the Division joined in battle against the Rocky Mountain locust, as in 1876. Later it encountered successive waves of such pests as the gypsy moth, the browntail moth, the cotton boll weevil, the San Jose Scale, the sprucebud worm—and so on. Pathologists are fighting the white-pine blister rust, the chestnut blight, smuts on wheat, the Dutch elm disease, and so forth. The two branches of bug and blight control are not always successful, of course; yet techniques have been developed, scientists trained, and organizations perfected until the American farmer has a powerful ally in his immemorial battle for a harvest.

Plant Quarantine

It was always known that much of our insect and plant-disease troubles originated in importations of goods from abroad. The obvious remedy was to halt such invasions at our borders. That was easy to say but difficult to accomplish, because it necessarily infringed upon private rights.

It was not until 1912 that a definite policy was formulated and adopted. That year the Plant Quarantine Act was passed, the Federal Horticultural Board was instituted, and various other protective measures were au-

thorized. Since then, all this work has been given into the hands of the Bureau of Entomology and Plant Quarantine. Thanks to its work, the importation of pests and blights has been greatly checked.

There have been, naturally, exceptions to its success. Witness the Japanese beetle and the Dutch elm disease. However, this Bureau is an efficient police force that protects our farms and gardens against invasion, and also, when trouble does develop, goes to work to eradicate or control the infestation.

One excellent example is the case of the white-pine blister rust. This enemy of our best timber tree proved a tough nut to crack. Then the Bureau's pathologists found that the fungus passed one stage of its life cycle on currant bushes. So, by eradicating currants from the vicinity of white-pine stands, the disease was wiped out. It was as simple as that; but the labor of discovering the cure was timetaking.

States co-operate in this work, of course; but it is the national Bureau that supplies the laboratory experts, the leaders of field crews, and the general administration.

Chemists

The farmer is also aided by the Department of Agriculture through its employment of chemists as watchdogs and as investigators. The problems of fertilizers, the task of rebuilding wornout soils, the development of industrial processes that will utilize farm crops, the difficulties involved in processing, storing, and distributing farm crops safely—all these and many more are attacked by chemists.

The service of the chemical laboratories is a silent one,

but its staffs stand behind the farmer every time he plants
a seed, harvests his crop, or sends it to market.

The Forest Service

The Department of Agriculture also provides various
specific agencies to aid the public welfare. One such is
the Forest Service, the organization which has the responsibility of protecting and developing our woodland
wealth. Up to about 1890 we did nothing much to save
our vanishing forests. We allowed anyone who wished to
cut or burn off what he pleased. Today the public has a
right to dictate the use of private forest land in the interest of the commonwealth. This modern idea would
have been decidedly unpopular before 1890. Moreover,
Americans seldom considered the waste of forest fires,
thinking nothing of the ravaging of millions upon millions of acres of trees each year. There were individuals
who pointed out the error of our ways, and crusades were
organized to save our forests—but for a long time, no one
of sufficient importance cared.

Eventually the protests were numerous enough to have
political strength, and in 1891 Congress made a small
beginning. It authorized the setting aside of forest reserves. This came in the nick of time. Already we had consumed something like four fifths of our forests. By 1905
many good citizens began to view the situation with alarm.
We were still cutting wood faster than it grew, and the
specter of a forestless nation, like China, appeared. So
Congress acted by creating the Forest Service. This con-
solidated all Federal forestry into one body.

Legislation, however, is but one step, and is often
powerless to stop an avalanche of popular custom. Things

went from bad to worse; and finally, in 1911, the Weeks Law was enacted. This, in effect, picked up a national forest policy which had been forgotten for almost a century. In 1799 Congress spent $200,000 to purchase forest reserves for the United States Navy; and in 1822 the Navy itself stepped in to prevent the cutting of timber on the public forest lands in Florida and Louisiana. The Navy needed oak for timber then, and pines for masts.

At last the Forest Service had a measure of authority. It could acquire forest land east of the Mississippi instead of being limited to the West; and so our national forests, that great reserve of woodland wealth, began to grow. Increase was slow at first. From 1911 to 1933 we acquired only 4,727,680 acres of forest lands. Then the Act of 1933 accelerated the development, and in one year (1937) we added 2,998,060 acres. In addition, the Forest Service began the work of protecting the forests, establishing fire towers to locate fires before they became serious, and fighting fires wherever they might develop.

The Weather Bureau

Another special service of the Department of Agriculture is the Weather Bureau. Recently it has been transferred to the Department of Commerce, but it was organized, developed, and maintained for more than half a century by the Department of Agriculture. This Bureau touches the life of every American every day. Its forecasts are often vital in saving many lives and billions of dollars worth of property—as in the New England hurricane of 1944.

For farmers, it predicts storms and frosts. For the citrus industry alone, a single frost forecast may save a million

dollars' worth of fruit. Cold-wave warnings enable farmers to protect their herds and their crops. Shippers and
warehouse men follow the forecasts hour by hour to protect goods from freezing in transit or from spoiling by
heat in storage.

Industry also depends upon the Weather Bureau.
Candymakers and textile-mill operators must know in
advance what the humidity will be. Engineers must know,
in winter, when it will be safe to pour a batch of concrete.
Storm warnings send small craft along the shores scud-
ding to safety and keep ships snug in the harbors. The importance of the Weather Bureau as the guardian of the
airways is demonstrated by the Bureau's transfer from
Agriculture to Commerce.

The Weather Bureau reaches up into the stratosphere
with robot radio weather stations, gaining information
where no man has yet soared. It works out better methods
of forecasting and is constantly seeking to improve its
services. Forecasting used to be an art; today it is a science. Tomorrow, instead of the 24-hour official forecast
and the 4-day outlook now current, the Bureau will predict seasonal conditions a year in advance!

Information, Please!

Two other important services of the Department of
Agriculture are the economic information service and the
marketing service.

For many years, until at least 1900, the emphasis of
agricultural development was placed upon production.
More food and better food was the idea. While such work
is still of prime importance, emphasis since the twentieth
century began has been shifted to marketing problems. In

this, statistics play an important part. So the Department has brought to a peak of high efficiency its crop-reporting and statistical work. By means of its market-news service in particular, news of crop conditions and details of stocks on hand has become the basis for general agricultural merchandising.

This news is now indispensable to the farmer. The reports are placed on the air in regular schedule. The farmer, sitting at home, not only can follow the prices being paid but, with the crop summaries, can plan intelligently even next year's planting as well as this year's marketing.

This service does not directly stabilize production nor does it smooth out price inequalities and prevent speculation; but it does provide the facts which can be used to accomplish these aims.

The Use of the Soil

Fundamentally, most of the work of the Department of Agriculture has been educational. The Government attempts to help the farmer by providing information. However, recently, the Department has had what may be considered police powers thrust upon it. The Roosevelt administration has obtained laws and regulations for the general benefit of the nation; and the Department has been required to enforce such of these as are concerned with the farmer. Not much, of course, has been attempted as yet—but it is a significant alteration in the relationship between the man on the farm and the man in Washington.

An example of this is the vexed and vital problem of soil conservation. On July 1, 1938, Henry A. Wallace, then Secretary of Agriculture, epitomized the problem

and the shift in the attitude of Government towards the farmer. He wrote:[8] "The earth is the mother of us all— plants, animals, and men. The phosphorus and calcium of the earth build our skeletons and nervous systems. Everything else our bodies need, except air and sun, comes from the earth.

"Nature treats the earth kindly. Man treats her harshly. He overplows the cropland, overgrazes the pasture land, and overcuts the timberland. He destroys millions of acres completely. He pours fertility year after year into the cities, which in turn pour what they do not use down the sewers into the rivers and the ocean. The flood problem, insofar as it is man-made, is chiefly the result of over-plowing, overgrazing, and overcutting of timber.

"This terribly destructive process is excusable in a young civilization. It is not excusable in the United States in the year 1938.

"We know what can be done; and we are beginning to do it. As individuals we are beginning to do the necessary things. As a nation, we are beginning to do them. The public is waking up, and just in time. In another thirty years it might have been too late.

"*The social lesson of soil waste is that no man has the right to destroy soil, even if he does own it in fee simple.* The soil requires a duty of man which we have been slow to recognize."

As expressed by Bushrod W. Allin, Director of the office of Land Use Co-ordination, the Government's program for beginning the solution of the problem of soil preservation is based upon five broad objectives: (1) greater stability and efficiency of farm production; (2) greater stability of natural resources—conservation of soil

and its fertility; better control of floods; and conservation of forests, water, forage, and wildlife; (3) greater stability of farm prices and income, and a better rural-urban balance; (4) greater security of tenure—a higher percentage of farmers owning their own land and a better tenure system for those who continue as tenants; (5) higher standards of rural living, and stability of rural communities, governments, and regions.

It may seem that this program is too ambitious. It has been criticized as such. But the situation is actually intricately interwoven with the life of the nation. It affects not the farmer alone, but every person in America, even if there be such as never set foot off concrete pavements.

For example, the areas affected by misuses of the soil are vast. Some 700,500,000 acres, thirty-seven per cent of the nation's area, have lost less than one fourth of the original surface through erosion. On forty-one per cent of the nation's face (some 755,600,000 acres) from one fourth to three fourths of the original surface soil has been lost. On about twelve per cent (225,000,000 acres) erosion has cost us the loss of more than three quarters of the soil surface. On three per cent (57,200,000 acres) the soil has been completely lost. The remaining seven per cent of our area (144,700,000 acres) is composed of rough lands of various kinds, mostly mountainous, and is not considered important agriculturally.

The word erosion includes loss by both wind and water; and no exact studies have been made of the relation between the two, or of the exact roles of overcropping, overgrazing, and overcutting of timber. But such studies as have been completed show beyond question the appalling results which misuse of the soil does produce. For

instance, measurements of the amount of water flowing from various types of surface show: from forested watersheds, the rate of flow was six cubic feet per second, per square mile; from abandoned farm land, the flow was 403 cubic feet per second, per square mile; from gullied pasture land, the flow was 785 cubic feet.

Thus the immediate need for better use of the soil is erosion control. Such things as reforestation, cover crops, withdrawal of steep gradients from cultivation, strip cropping, contour plowing—all these have their role. Dams and storage basins can be built, and are being built, to impound abnormal rains.

Farm Banking

But all this is only the beginning, for in the last analysis, it is the way in which each farmer uses his soil that matters. And the way in which he does so is the result of economical, social, and educational compulsions. Correction of farm conditions is even more necessary than soil conservation. Typical of this need is the dreadful system of tenancy—and, of course, the still worse evil of sharecropping.

To summarize: In the first quarter of the twentieth century, in this wealthy nation of ours about 42 per cent of our farm families did not own the land they worked. They had become tenants. Again, more than 900,000 farm families were trying to keep body and soil together on gross incomes of less than $400 a year![9]

The solutions of this situation lie beyond the period of this chapter, but it was in the period just before the Great Depression of 1929 that the condition became apparent

and the first preliminary steps were taken in the long battle to restore our farm prosperity.

The first reactions were, largely, to provide financial remedies. First there was the establishment of the Federal Reserve System in 1913. Not primarily a farm bill, it did attempt to help farmers by providing for the reasonable expansion of currency when needed, by the rediscounting of agricultural paper for six months, and by giving national banks permission to loan money on farm mortgages.

In 1916 came the second step, the inauguration of the Federal Farm Loan Bank, organized to give the farmer longer credit than six months. If a farmer needed money to finance his planting, it would be more than six months before he could repay it. He had to wait until late fall when his crops were harvested and sold and payment had been received.

Ordinary bankers did not like long-term farm loans. As a result, such farm loans fell into the hands of private groups and individuals, who were freer than the banks to charge exorbitant interest. Again, the Farm Loan Banks relieved the farmers from their traditional position of being under the thumbs of local firms and dealers. These dealers advanced money that the farmer was obligated to repay by selling his crops at low rates.

The Farm Loan Banks were established in Springfield, Massachusetts; Baltimore, Maryland; Columbia, South Carolina; Louisville, Kentucky; New Orleans, Louisiana; St. Louis, Missouri; St. Paul, Minnesota; Omaha, Nebraska; Wichita, Kansas; Houston, Texas; Berkeley, California; Spokane, Washington; and Washington, D. C.

The system provided an administrative board known as

the Federal Farm Loan Board and a subsidiary organization, the National Farm Loan Association. Money was loaned to farmers up to 50 per cent of the value of the land, and to 20 per cent of the value of permanent improvements for financing the purchase of land, livestock, equipment, and the usual farm operations.

The Act also provided for Joint Stock Land Banks, financed privately. These private banks were incorporated independently. They could make loans to farmers for any purpose, and could go beyond the $10,000 limit of the publicly owned system.

Well-designed, if complicated, these land banks did not meet the farmers' need completely; so in 1923 the Agricultural Credits Act was passed. This established twelve Federal Intermediate Credit Banks, which do not deal with farmers but serve as banks for the rediscount of agricultural paper for periods in excess of six months and up to three years.

Thus genuine financial service was afforded the farmer. He could, if he wished, ignore the "loan sharks" who had fattened on him for so long. The new system provides for regular amortization payments. It is to be hoped that, at long last, the farmer may rid himself of the load of debt under which he has staggered ever since the time of the Pilgrims—who came to America on borrowed funds.

Colleges and Experiment Stations

Together with the many services of the Department of Agriculture and the recent banking organizations, the Government made still a third response to the needs of the farmers—direct education.

The program began in 1862 with the Morrill Act. This

established a "land grant" college or colleges in each State for the purpose of instructing students in agriculture and mechanical arts. To endow these institutions, each college was given, out of the public domain, grants of 30,000 acres for each Senator and each Representative in Congress. The individual States, in most instances, supplemented the endowments and arranged for annual financing.

The East had been well enough served educationally by such institutions as Harvard, Yale, Princeton, Penn, and the rest. But most of the nation in the South and in States lying west of the Appalachian Mountains benefited tremendously from this policy of the Government of helping the farmer. Much of America's educational system still rests firmly upon the foundation thus established. However, it was soon apparent that something more than book learning was needed to make good farmers better. So in 1877 Congress provided for the establishment of Experiment Stations.

All through the years, privately operated experiment stations, like that of the Massachusetts Horticultural Society, had proved their worth. Then, in 1875, Orange Judd, publisher of the *American Agriculturist,* had generously co-operated with the State of Connecticut in establishing a publicly owned experiment station in Wesleyan University, at Middletown. Professor W. O. Atwater organized the station and made such a good beginning that farmers and their friends everywhere became enthusiastic. So, in 1877, experiment stations were established by Congress in conjunction with each State's agricultural college or university. These stations proved their worth and became an integral part of the nation's service to the farmer.

Specifically, they applied science to the local needs of the farmers, solved their immediate problems as far as possible, and also served as a means of distributing news of farming—showing the farmer and also "telling" him. In the South the stations worked with cotton, in Texas with cattle, in Maine with potatoes, in Louisiana with sugar cane, and so forth.

Subsequently, the Department of Agriculture established other and specialized types of stations, such as the Northeast Forest Experiment Station at New Haven, Connecticut, and the Forest Products Laboratory at Madison, Wisconsin. But the original experiment station organization has remained the backbone of the work. Thus by its organization of Government-managed and Government-financed services on behalf of the farmer, by the Department of Agriculture, by the Federal Banks, and by colleges and experiment stations, the Government has responded to the needs of the farmer.

In recent days the Government has tended to shift from education and service towards control—but that is a matter for the final section of this brief history.

[1] Chew, Arthur P. *Response of Government to Agriculture*. Washington. 1937
[2] Clark, William H. *Boston Sunday Globe*. October 29, 1939
[3] Revised Statutes. Sect. 520
[4,5] Richardson, J. L. *Messages and Papers of the Presidents*. Washington. 1897
[6] Plunkett, Sir Horace. *Rural Life Problem of the U. S.* New York. 1913
[7,9] Chew, *Op. cit.*
[8] *Soils and Men*. United States Department of Agriculture. Washington. 1938

CHAPTER XVIII

REGIONAL DEVELOPMENT

LET US ride with the sun across America on a summer morning in 1929. The dawn first finds a potato farmer, far north in Maine's Aroostook County. Then, passing over sleek herds in New England's green pastures, it reaches the seaboard cities. Around them lie the crowded acres of the market gardeners.

Nearing Washington, D. C., the dawn passes over orchards and great flocks of hens and ducks along the Eastern Shore. Beyond are the tobacco acres and the cornfields of the South. The sun reaches fields of cotton and of peanuts—and then orchards and more orchards, peach and pecan. All down the sandy arm of Florida lying between the Atlantic and the Gulf of Mexico, it glitters upon the golden fruit of orange and grapefruit trees.

These are glimpses of the mighty panorama of the Atlantic Coast of the United States, a 2,000-mile reach of States from the Northeast to the Southwest.

The sun speeds straight toward the West, climbs over the ridges of the Appalachians and swoops on over the broad, level Midland empire. Forested hills give place to level grasslands. Rivers are wider and more leisurely. Farms are larger. Miles of golden wheat gleam in the North.

To the south of them lies a parallel belt of corn and,

247

farther yet, cotton plantations. There are the sugar-cane fields in Mississippi; the citrus farms in Texas; and beyond the Mississippi, the tawny grass of the ranches, dotted with clusters of horned cattle and of placid sheep. Beyond the prairies the Rockies thrust themselves into the sky. Here are masses of gray rock, thinly thatched with trees, and higher peaks crowned white with everlasting snow.

In the green valleys are more cattle and sheep. To the south the land is barer, save here and there where thread-like ditches bring down over many miles the impounded waters of the melting snows high in the hills. Along these ditches, startlingly green and luxuriant among the sands, are the irrigated farms—production won from the reluctant desert.

The light crosses the mountains, and suddenly the Pacific opens ahead. The sun gilds the oranges and lemons of California, colors the apples and warms the grain fields of Oregon and Washington, and touches the magnificent forests among the coastal hills. Three thousand miles, from East to West—a four-hour journey for the sun. It was all wilderness three hundred years ago.

The story of this transformation is not one of farms alone. Industry, commerce, and transportation, constantly altering and developing, are closely interwoven with the story of farming. We are accustomed to divide America into States, our traditional political pattern. Today that simplification is outmoded. This story can best be broken down for consideration in terms of regions. Even a volume for each such section would not be adequate; so in this outline of high lights, only a sketch of each region can be attempted.

The Northeast

In New England, New York, and the rest of that section, the seventy years from 1861 to 1929 brought profound changes. Once the very heart of America, agriculturally no less than industrially, socially, and politically, the region lost its pre-eminence as the nation developed.

Farming, in particular, became relatively unimportant. It was largely because of the greed with which mill, factory, and shop devoured capital and men that farming was displaced as a major activity. Cities grew tremendously, for the Northeast had the capital and the intelligent labor required by manufacturing and distribution. Farm after farm went out of general production. Where once there were fields of wheat, corn, buckwheat, oats, rye, and the rest, grass grew undisturbed. Over areas great in the aggregate, the wilderness marched back, enfolding the farms wrested from it by sweat and sacrifice. By 1930 there was more wilderness in New England than there had been in 1800. There are more wild deer today in Maine, for example, than there have been since the days of earliest settlement.

Of course, agriculture was not abandoned entirely. The recession was only relative. Industrialized, New England was in the position of producing barely enough food to feed itself for one week out of each year, save for a few items like milk, potatoes, and cranberries. But in the most favorable sections, agriculture continued to flourish and in some spots to become more successful than before. In the aggregate, Yankee farm production is still great. In the farthest hills, mixed farming continued on something of the colonial subsistence level. But specialized forms of farming developed to replace the old general agriculture.

One new type of special farming was dairying. About half the farms embraced this activity, in whole or in part. The cool summers, the even distribution of precipitation throughout the year, and the proximity of thriving cities needing fluid milk, plus a network of transportation facilities, combined to create almost ideal dairying conditions.

So excellent was the market, save when it was flooded by overproduction, that the Northeast concentrated upon this fluid milk. The farmers did not bother to make much butter or cheese. Today, even cream has to be imported into New England (from Wisconsin), to say nothing of condensed and evaporated milk.

A second new type of farming was market gardening. These farms, most of them within a very short haul of city markets, began to supply city folks with fresh vegetables and fruit. Prices were high enough to make heavy fertilization profitable; hence began the intense cultivation of the soil. Great hothouses annually produce highly lucrative out-of-season crops such as tomatoes, cucumbers, grapes, roses, chrysanthemums, and carnations.

Then there developed geographically limited special types of farming. One is potato growing in Maine's Aroostook County. This county has nearly as much land in potatoes as exists within the entire area of Massachusetts. This peculiar specialization grew up because the soil and the climate of Aroostook are perfect for potatoes. The rich soils of the Connecticut River valley proved similarly excellent for two special crops, the onion and tobacco. This last is not the type grown in the South, but a high grade variety with large, silky leaves that make excellent cigar wrappings. Also, the climate of the Northeast gives

Courtesy Soil Conservation Service

DIGGING POTATOES IN MAINE'S AROOSTOOK COUNTY

apples very superior quality. They are not so highly colored nor as large as those from the Pacific Northwest; but the Yankee apple has firmer flesh and an exquisite flavor. Few Yankee farmers bother to care for their trees properly; the spray schedule is arduous. But in areas like the Nashoba Valley in Massachusetts, apples are usually a very profitable crop. Asparagus, cranberries, and mushrooms are also local specialties.

The important fact is this: agriculture declined very greatly in importance in this area in the seventy years after the Civil War. What remained, however, through specialization, became solidly based. In the Northeast, farmers for the most part own their own land. There are few tenant farmers; and the proportion of farmers who own autos, radios, telephones, bathtubs, and the like, is very high compared to the number in the rest of America.

The South

No section of America has changed so much in these seventy years as has the South. The war blasted the bright, unsound glory of King Cotton. Planters lost their slaves, tools, cattle, homes, and in many cases their land. In reconstruction, many a farmer plunged so deeply into debt that it was a generation or more before agriculture could lift its head. Many a problem is still not satisfactorily adjusted even now.

Probably because of the war, the South lost fifty per cent of its wealth. A historian wrote on this point:

"Plantations that brought $100,000 to $150,000 before the war . . . sold at $6,000 or $10,000 or hung upon the hands of the planter and his factor at any price. The ruin seemed universal and complete, and the old planta-

tion system, it seemed, had perished utterly and forever." [1]

Many of the old plantations were broken up into small farms of around ten acres. These small holdings were used by both white and Negro owners for the cultivation of cotton—still the cash crop of the South. Thus came into being the "poor white" class of the region—small family groups, handicapped by lack of capital, land, and labor. Actually, this division of the great plantations into small units was the beginning of the agricultural regeneration of the South. But many difficult years had to pass before this became evident. Instead, the freehold farmer found himself obscured by the vicious establishment of the "share-cropper."

The share-cropper institution is now a modern problem. Some large farmers held onto their lands; and speculators acquired big acreages at very low prices. Instead of farming for themselves, these profiteers rented out their land in small patches to poor white and poor Negro farmers who did all the work for a certain share of the returns. The system was organized, commonly, on a tripartite basis. One third went for the land; one for seed, fertilizer, and mules; and one to the share-cropper.

The white families fared badly, for they had to maintain a somewhat higher standard of living than the newly freed slaves. But the Negroes, more careless, generally, fared badly, too. They now had no one to drive them or to lead them, as had been the custom. They barely made enough even in good years to provide a shack for shelter, rags, for clothing, and "turnip greens and side meat" for daily food.

The evil of this system came about not only because of the low income resulting, but because the unfortunate

tenants borrowed, ten months of the year, for food, clothing, and nearly everything else they needed. In return they pledged their share of the harvest. Since the harvest had to be sold through the creditor, the sharecropper system came to mean virtual peonage. Often families sank so deeply into perennial debt that they forgot even to dream of independence. The quality of their work in the fields could not remain high under such perpetual discouragement.

By 1880 the South had managed to rid itself of the worst abuses it had suffered; by 1900, although still badly enough off, the South had so lifted itself by its bootstraps that it was ready for the better times which came at the turn of the century, when cotton prices improved. This was stimulus enough to break for a time the sad cycle of poor labor, poor methods, poor crops, and poor prices. Easier credit developed; and then the industrialization of the South added its potent influence. Poor whites could find employment in cotton mills, hosiery factories, lumber mills, and so on. Share-cropping remains a blight yet to be exorcised; but the southern farmer today is at least fairly well off compared to the farmer of post-bellum days, particularly since he is now on a sound economic basis—which was not the case in the days of slavery.

Not only did cotton income improve, but tobacco growing also staged a remarkable comeback. This is due partly to improved methods of culture, but more to the wide development of the cigarette habit. Not only does tobacco find a ready market, but cigarette factories provide considerable employment, especially for unskilled women and girls.

The South also embarked upon a deliberately planned

program of farming diversification. This has had excellent results among products like peanuts, peaches, pecans, and potatoes. The list is long and promising. Climate also has been capitalized. The famous winter resorts in Virginia, the Carolinas, and, most particularly, in Florida (called the Empire of the Sun) have given southern farm products a veritable boom.

Florida is now a wealthy State agriculturally. Oranges, grapefruit, winter strawberries, beans, tomatoes, cauliflower—the list is long. Intelligent State promotion has restored cattle ranching, formerly very important, and also has encouraged many other occupations, such as lumbering, and even industrial activities.

Sugar

Sugar farming is being considered last because of its relative unimportance on the national scale. In antebellum days and for years afterwards the rewarding cultivation of this giant grass was in the hands of the Louisiana Creoles and "Cajuns"—the former, descendants of the original French settlers; the latter, the Arcadians driven out of Nova Scotia by the British.

Sugar cane is a special crop, and hence its culture was long limited to narrow strips along the banks of the Mississippi, the delta rivers, and the bayous behind. There were great estates, some of 10,000 acres, on such holdings; but only about ten per cent of the land was available for cultivation. Slaves died quickly in these malarial sections. This fact increased overhead and capitalization, so that few farmers had the $400,000 to $500,000 needed to establish a big sugar plantation. However, these great es-

Courtesy U. S. D. of A.

SOUTHERN MANSION ON A LOUISIANA SUGAR PLANTATION

tablishments did well for a time; ten per cent per annum was an ordinary return.

After the war the sugar plantations recovered almost immediately, for the North wanted sugar, and the market was brisk. However, even then Louisiana could not produce nearly enough sugar to meet the demand. Although cane sugar in the United States has continued to be a major crop in the limited area where it can be grown, it is now so overshadowed as to be of minor national importance.

America consumes sugar in vast quantities. Many individuals eat as much as a hundred pounds a year, counting candy, beverages, and sweetened foods. We have three ways of meeting the problem of sugar supply. The first is importing. Cuba, the West Indies, Hawaii, and the Philippines each send us tremendous tonnages. Because of the war (and rationing) recent figures are lacking, but the United States normally imports about three quarters of the sugar consumed.[2]

The second solution to our need for sweetness comes from the chemists. By treatment with heat and acids, cornstarch can be made into a sweet substance. A great amount of this corn sugar is being produced, but it is ordinarily used in industry by confectioners, bakers, and the like.

The third way in which we get sugar is from the sugar beet. It is by no means as rich a source of sugar as sugar cane, but it does very well. It is not a crop of the South, for sugar beets as a rule can be grown only in cool climates; but it can well be mentioned here, even if out of place and time.

Sugar-beet culture began in France and Germany early in the nineteenth century, when the Napoleonic wars cut

off importations of sweet products from abroad. Liberally subsidized by the several governments concerned, by
1860 the sugar beet (it is a different variety from the ordinary table beet) was producing a quarter of the world's
sugar; in 1882, one half; and in 1900, nearly two thirds.[3]
In reality, France and Germany, instead of importing
sugar, today export it (war times aside) to the rest of the
world.

In America beet sugar did not interest the farmer at
first. It is a crop that requires much handwork of a very
low grade, such as the thinning of the seedlings. The price
for sugar is low; hence there is a very low wage for field
workers and but a scant return for the land employed for
the farmer. The beet sugar industry in Europe was often
a political football, and it also has been artificially stimulated here. Thus the American farmer has also become a
sugar-beet producer.

The first successful sugar-beet farming was begun in
California about 1890. Since that time the beet has become cultivated in most of the prairie and mountain
States. By 1907[4] beet sugar production exceeded that of
cane sugar; and since that time beets have continued important. However, both beet and cane production of sugar
in continental United States normally totals only about
one quarter of the sugar this nations consumes.[5]

The Middle West

The Middle West has become the granary of the nation and of much of the rest of the world. Wheat and
corn reach from East to West in overlapping belts; the
former generally somewhat to the north of the latter.

Corn has remained at the head of the list. The United

States grows perhaps 75 per cent of the world's maize. It constitutes about 50 per cent of our national cereal wealth. Of course, comparatively little of it (sweet corn excepted) is now eaten by humans. Nor do we export much of it, in contrast to wheat. Some of it is concentrated into whiskey and some of it into starch and sugars; but a very large part of it is fed to animals—transformed into beef, pork, poultry, and eggs for human consumption.

This corn-feeding division of farming ties in closely with animal husbandry, of course. Iowa, Kansas, Nebraska, and to an extent Missouri, Illinois, and Indiana, produce annually some four to five billion dollars' worth of meat, lard, and related products. These are sources of farm wealth which would be impossible if it were not for the neighboring expansive acres of rustling corn.

Wheat

Wheat is only slightly less important to the American farmer than corn. In bread, cake, porridge, or pastry, we all eat it in some form at every meal. In colonial times, New England and New York wheat fed what there was of English America. By 1860, wheat had become centered in Illinois; from there it moved on to the West and the North.

Until Civil War times, our wheat had been a soft winter variety which could not withstand severe cold or prolonged drought. Then the hard red species was introduced. This wheat, through multiplication of varieties and by an adaptation of milling facilities, has enlarged the wheat-growing area even into the bitterly cold open lands of Canada. A durum wheat, from Russia, more recently introduced than the red, has also enlarged wheat

farming and made it more profitable. This strong, disease-resistant stock has made the Dakotas as important wheat States as the more naturally favored Kansas, Nebraska, and Iowa.

Much of the story of wheat, formerly the less profitable of farm crops, depends upon the advance of mechanization, which has transformed its culture. This topic is discussed in the next chapter. Both corn and wheat are included in the story of distilling and brewing. Here is an important market for the farmer. The vats of the brewers and the retorts of the distillers consume huge quantities of corn and wheat. Then, too, the growing industrial demand for non-beverage alcohol, as in the making of synthetic rubber and in other new and coming chemurgical processes, indicate an even greater consumption ahead.

Milk

Like corn, the dairy industry is widespread throughout the nation. Milk cattle, lean and pitiful creatures, are forced to feed even upon the scanty grass of southern Florida. But in Wisconsin and in Minnesota the dairy industry has become concentrated. Not only has this region a fluid milk industry comparable to that of the Northeast, but it supports a mammoth milk-processing business for butter, cream, cheese, condensed milk, evaporated milk, and dehydrated milk. These two States are too far from the great markets of America for fluid milk shipment. Ideally located for milk production, they can profitably engage in various milk-processing activities. Machines were invented and creameries were organized. With such a volume of production as developed, the old

Courtesy U. S. D. of A.

MODERN DAIRY FARM AMONG NEW JERSEY HILLS

style of haphazard farm-home processing was no longer economical.

Since butterfat thus became of paramount importance, the breeding of better cows was greatly energized, as were methods of refrigerating and processing. From a humble beginning in the farm kitchen, dairying has thus become a highly scientific and efficiently managed business.

Added impetus to dairying in this region came with modern techniques for canning and dehydrating fluid milk. Even the most rigid care in production and the most painstaking methods of distribution cannot keep milk from going sour. Thus raw or fluid milk, even with Pasteurization (which checks for a while bacterial development), is fundamentally a product for strictly local consumption. Farmers knew that the market for preserved milk would be world-wide, if it could be worked out. So the milk canning industry began about 1860, when condensed milk first appeared. Much water is removed from the milk, and some sugar is added. Then came the process of canning milk without sugar merely by evaporation, to reduce its bulk about fifty per cent. Lately, an advance has been made in dehydration, which removes all the water and makes it possible to ship milk anywhere. Much of the successful development of this last process has been war-inspired.

By processing in its various forms from powder to concentrated cheese, milk is now no longer limited to local markets. Dairying is one of our major farm industries.

The Far West

In the Far West, in contrast with most of the United States, precipitation is scant. It seldom passes twenty

inches a year. New England, in contrast, averages about forty inches. The reason is that the prevailing atmospheric circulation—scientific word for the alternation of storms and calms—passes eastward over the mountains. To do this, the air must rise. In rising, it is cooled; and thus, because of physical laws governing the amount of water vapor air can hold, most of the water evaporated from the Pacific falls along the Pacific coast. Thus, parts of the Far West suffer from drought.

Between 1860 and 1885, as previously described, this semi-arid land was America's great ranching region. By 1885 homesteaders had pushed into the jealously guarded cattle preserves, and the Great Plains were opened so that wheat could be planted. This was probably one of America's major mistakes. As long as the age-old sod remained, despite the grazing of cattle and the close nibbling of sheep, the soil was firmly anchored. The plow of the wheat farmers turned up the soil, bared it to the drying sun and wind, and so disaster eventually came, in the form of dust storms.

Perhaps this wide, western area is suited only for cattle. Certainly ordinary farming there cannot be permanently successful under natural conditions. When the rain cycle is wet, then wheat can thrive. But when the rain cycle swings to dry, then starvation and bitter poverty are inevitable.

But there is the new technique of dry-farming, which consists of making use of every reluctant drop of rain and flake of snow that falls. Fields are dyked and channeled after each harvest, to impound the snow. Weeds which steal moisture in the subsoil are carefully eliminated. Usually, fields are cultivated only every second or third

year, so that the thirsty ground can absorb water and thus restore the water table against the single year of use. Perhaps this technique may make it possible for more favored areas of the Far West to maintain an agriculture. That remains to be seen. Surely unbroken grass would be best for much of the land in that region.

Irrigation

Irrigation is proposed as a panacea. The art of bringing water into dry soil began with the Spanish settlers five centuries back. Modern irrigation began, however, only in 1877 with the passage of the Desert Land Act. This Act had unfortunate consequences; for while it did benefit ranchers and sheep raisers, homesteaders were often robbed by rascally speculators.

"The companies have erected dams that are too flimsy," protested many of the homesteaders. "The ditches are inadequate; the companies have sold us this so-called reclaimed land at extortion prices; and look at the small trickle of water that is available!"

The homesteaders' protests were eventually heard in Washington; and the Carey Act of 1894 improved conditions by making water rights an actual part of land titles. In addition, States were permitted to set aside desert lands and to permit private companies to construct irrigation facilities only under the eyes of a State commission established to protect the farmers. Homesteaders could buy such reclaimed lands at fifty cents an acre, plus a sliding charge for water rights, according to the cost of the particular project. When the cost of the project was thus refunded, the company was discharged, and the ownership of the entire system passed to the farmers themselves.

This was a remarkable advance, but it had the fault of not being sufficiently profitable to attract private capital; and it did not provide for repairs in case of serious damage to the system by floods.

Pressure by the farmers resulted in the Reclamation Act of 1902. This put the Federal Government into the irrigation business. For a time the Act failed to produce the benefits which its proponents had visioned. Settlers who had bought land under the Act and were accordingly entitled to three feet of water a year for their acres, waited and waited in vain. So the Government was compelled to toss millions of dollars into what seemed an insatiable maw—often without commensurate return being possible. Eventually, however, the system was ironed out. No longer is water brought at vast expense to acres which, for one reason or another, cannot produce profitable crops.

Still, the irrigation business is something of a luxury, which the Government supports for the interest of comparatively few farmers. Of course, the projects recently completed and projected may make a profound difference. At any event, to June 1930, the last year for which figures are available because of World War II, the Government had spent $347,224,082 on thirty-four irrigation and reclamation projects in sixteen States, thus watering about 5,000,000 acres. Annual production from this land is estimated to be about $161,000,000.[6]

The Pacific Coast

In the North, in the States carved out of the Oregon Territory, the forest remains of vast importance. There still stands our only remaining primeval timber of any

considerable extent. As for farming, the States here are very rich and prosperous agriculturally. Wheat reaches impressive totals, but the area also has a developing and widely diversified farming organization. Here is one of the most blessed climates in the world, with plenty of rain, well-distributed; summers are cool enough for comfort; and winters usually mild.

Actually, here is a farmer's paradise. One proof of this, dull statistics aside, is the fact that the States of Oregon and Washington are becoming centers of bulb production. It is from the West Coast that all America obtains its tulips, narcissus, iris, and other spring flowering bulbs. The region is rich in sheep and cattle, and its apple orchards are known the world over. Actually, these States can grow just about every crop known in the world except those of the subtropics and the tropics. In spite of this, the slender population of farmers has held these States back. The farms, in general, are small and owned free and clear. As transportation improves and local markets are developed more largely, the farmer in the new Northwest should be well rewarded for his efforts.

In California, farming varies sharply from the cool and humid northern to the hot and dry southern sections. In the northern part, wheat, corn, wool, and rice are commonly produced. Lumbering and truck farming help to make San Francisco one of the world's greatest cities. There is also the grape industry, with its wine and its raisins. In the southern section there is the greatest of all citrus industries. Most of America's lemons come from California, as do a goodly portion of oranges, grapefruit, and limes. This great industry had its start when the United States Department of Agriculture in 1873 sent two

navel orange trees from Bahia, Brazil, to Riverside, California.

Mrs. Eliza C. Tibbetts planted the trees at her home. At first the trees, probably of the Portuguese *Selecta* variety, were merely curiosities. Today, one of these trees, still standing where Mrs. Tibbetts planted it, is a monument almost as jealously guarded as Faneuil Hall in Boston. It may well be so honored, for from it came most of the orange trees now strewn across the southern half of California.

Today there are 300,000 acres planted to oranges, lemon, and grapefruit trees; and some 200,000 citizens of the State, farmers and dealers, depend upon the trees for their living. On the average about $100,000,000 a year come to California for her fruit. California produces 60 per cent of all the oranges and 95 per cent of all the lemons consumed in the United States.[7]

This development is not all due to the magical soil and climate of California. The farmers built up their prosperity by establishing the California Fruit Growers Exchange, a co-operative marketing organization of 13,330 California and Arizona growers, a group growing 75 per cent of the two States' production of oranges, lemons, and grapefruit.

The co-operative came into being primarily as a marketing organization. Farmers were careless about their culture and indifferent about their packing. With their major market 3,000 miles to the east, this was almost a fatal fault. So the Exchange was created to establish grades, perfect packing, and organized distribution. It also enlarged the national market by skillful advertising; and shortly it had changed citrus fruit from a holiday lux-

GOLD FROM THE SOIL OF CALIFORNIA

ury to a daily breakfast-table habit for the entire nation. The Exchange also mastered cultural ills. Insects and diseases had to be fought. Water was needed for irrigation. Frost protection devices and organization had to be developed. No one farmer could have accomplished anything of importance in these fields; but together, the farmers belonging to the Exchange worked them out swiftly, efficiently, and economically.

Finally the Exchange branched out into services. It built mills to produce packing boxes. It educated members in the latest scientific developments. Among other things, it founded a research laboratory which not only meets the daily needs of citrus farmers but is constantly seeking new products for new markets, concentrates, perfumes, oils, citrate salts, pectin, and so on.[8]

Potatoes to Oranges

Thus over the vast area of the United States the farmer has established himself. His houses range from the little white "Cape Cods" of New England to the gay stucco bungalows of California. His products run from potatoes in misty Maine to oranges in the almost rainless southwestern desert. He has had his troubles—and he will have more—but our nation, 130,000,000 of us, not only has more than it can eat but annually feeds much of the world besides. America may have only one man in every three on its farms—but we still have a multitude of farms, and the farmer generally is doing a grand job.

[1] Grady, H. W. *Harper's Magazine.* Vol. 53, p. 721.
[2, 3, 4, 5] Day, Clive. *A History of Commerce.* 4th Edition. New York. 1924
[6] Bogart. *Op. cit.*
[7, 8] *The Story of California Oranges.* California Fruit Growers Exchange. Los Angeles. 1936

CHAPTER XIX

FROM MUSCLE TO MOTOR

ONE Saturday afternoon in December, 1930, a half dozen farmers of a New Hampshire hill town were sitting about in the general store. Each farmer present was a great-great-grandson of a man who had walked up from the Massachusetts Bay Colony two hundred years before with axe and rifle and cut and burned clear the acres still being worked.

The farmers talked about the depression. It didn't worry them much right then. Their barns were filled with hay and corn for the stock. Their cellars and pantries were filled with food for their families. They could get along without the world for the winter. They talked about the changes which had come over farming around their small town.

"A farmer has to be a pretty smart man nowadays," spoke up one. "We have to be farmers, and electricians, plumbers, blacksmiths, masons, carpenters, salesmen, and business executives, too. We have to know something about everything, if we are going to get by."

"We have to be capitalists first of all," said another farmer. "We need money and lots of it to farm successfully today. I have to buy a new tractor, come spring. I hope my maple sugar will pay for it. Got to have machines —and they cost money."

Farming in the United States had changed profoundly. The harsh fact faced by all farmers was that they "had to have machines—and machines cost money."

1861-1929

The era ending in 1861 was featured by the gradual invention and the slow acceptance of agricultural machinery. The period between the Civil War and the Great Depression was characterized by the replacement of animal power with that of motors.

Mechanization became necessary. To make a living, farmers had to get more and more land into cultivation and to crop that land more and more effectively. The margin of profit grew ever narrower; costs mounted and prices fell; so that to make a dollar, the farmer had to produce several times as much as did his father and grandfather. Machines were the only answer.

The Combine

Probably the greatest development was the combine for the harvesting of grain. By 1880, when most of the basic patents were granted, 10,000 patents relating to harvesting machinery were recorded in the United States alone.[1]

The reason for this advance was not merely the natural improvement of the clumsy, grain-harvesting contraptions of 1860. It was because the acreage devoted to wheat, corn, oats, rye, and the rest so multiplied that efficient machines were necessary, in view of the labor shortage incident to the Civil War. Cereals must be harvested promptly. There can be no delay when the grain is ripe. Even a brief loss of time may mean the difference between a prosperous year and bankruptcy.

Planting and cultivation are not so urgent; and thus, while seed drills, plows, and cultivators were improved, they did not have the spectacular and triumphant career of the reaping machines, which culminated in the combines. These giants epitomize the spirit of America as well as do our vast industrial establishments and our city laboratories.

The ante-bellum reapers, such as McCormick's, were mowers for cutting grain. The Marsh-type canvas belt was only a contrivance to make binding more rapid. Human hands were still necessary with these machines.

Farmers needed a machine that would bind the sheaves of grain. For years, various inventors worked hopefully with cord, twine, wire, and even metal bands, but only in 1874 did an inventor, Charles B. Withington of Janesville, Wisconsin, perfect a wire binder. McCormick, purchasing the patent, marketed a combination reaper and binder. At last, any boy who could drive a horse could cut and bind a field of wheat.

Then, in 1875, John F. Appleby of DePere, Wisconsin, perfected the twine binder and sold his patent to William Deering, who knew the twine binder to be superior to the wire binder, for twine was cheaper and had proved to be better than wire.

By 1880 Deering was the leading reaper-binder maker. McCormick was faced with serious competition, for his wire binder was no longer purchased by farmers. So McCormick arranged to use the Appleby twine binder, and by 1881 was as prosperous as ever.

Still another step was needed for real mechanization. The thresher was an independent, cumbersome machine. Inventors went to work, and within five years several

threshers were designed and tested. By 1890 they had been united with reapers and binders into one huge machine—the combine.

The McCormick reaper cut the grain, the Appleby binder tied the stems into neat bundles, the threshers hammered out the grain, fans winnowed away the chaff, and blowers removed the straw. Mechanical fingers poured the grain into sacks, sewed up the sacks, weighed them, and then dumped them into carts to be pulled to elevators and the market. At last, thanks to mechanization, every step in the placing of bread on the tables of the world had become mechanical.

For some years these great combines were tugged across the fields by horses. Gradually, steam engines came into use, engines fired by the straw pouring out of the thresher sections. These were ponderous contrivances, rolling along over the soft fields on wheels which were eighteen feet high.

Steam was dangerous, for the flames under the boilers were likely to set fire to the fields of standing grain. So the advent of the internal combustion gasoline engine was very welcome.

This engine was not a completely satisfactory innovation, however, until the tractor was developed—of which, more later. But, with motor power, the combine was at last complete. No more muscle power, human or animal, was needed. One engineer alone sat at the wheel and the levers; and machinery did the work, replacing the toil and sweat of man.

The result is demonstrated in the following comparison between the harvesting of 200 acres of wheat averaging 20 bushels to the acre in 1830 and in 1930:[2 and 3]

Time Required per Acre in Hours and Minutes

1830, Hand Labor			1930, Machine Farming		
Breaking Ground	6 and 40		Plowing by tractor	0 and 54
Sowing Seed	1 and 25		Disking by tractor	0 and 15
Covering seed	2 and 50		Harrowing by tractor	0 and 6
Reaping, Binding	20 and 0		Seeding by tractor	0 and 15
Hauling to barn	4 and 0		Harvesting and threshing,	
Threshing	13 and 20		combine and tractor	0 and 36
Winnowing	12 and 0		Hauling by truck to	
Sacking and Sewing	4 and 0		storage	0 and 18
	64 and 15			2 and 24

The Tractor

Much of this miracle, one in which speed was essential, was accomplished by tractors, which have a long history behind them. They are the result of the ideas and applications of many men.

The modern gasoline-powered unit is the direct descendant of the steam-powered engine. These steam engines, developed to haul combines, prairie plows, and cultivators, were partly the work of two men, Jacob Price and Daniel Best, who flourished in the nineties, as well as of Benjamin Holt of Stockton, California.

The problem that vexed the operators of steam engines was that of traction. The belching and puffing monsters often mired down in the soft soil of the farms. To keep them moving, wheels as large as eighteen feet in height were built, their rims cleated with heavy steel angle iron. Even so, the wheels often spun uselessly in the mud.

The solution was known—the so-called lag-bed tractor, a sort of endless-belt arrangement which moves around with the wheels. It lays down a steel track before the wheels and picks it up behind them.

The principle was simple, but the application was dif-

ficult. More than a hundred patents for lag-beds of one kind or another were granted in the United States before 1901. That year Alvin Lombard, a lumberman living in Waterville, Maine, brought out the ancestor of the now familiar "caterpillar" tread. Lombard's tractor was for pulling logs out of the woods. In California, Holt in 1903 created the present type of caterpillar tread.

This tread, when finally adapted to farm use, solved the problem of traction for the steam engine at the exact time when there was no longer any need for steam traction in the harvest fields. The gasoline motor, perfected for autos and trucks, was simply placed on a special chassis equipped with the caterpillar treads—and there was the modern tractor ready to go to work.

The farm tractor has also developed through the perfection of the pneumatic rubber tire. Many tractors, especially of the smaller types for individual farm use, came to have ordinary wheels instead of the lag-bed. Such wheels gain traction because of the cleated design of thin rubber tires. They bite deep into the mud and pull any plow, cutter, or wagon hitched to their tails.

Other Machines

While the tractor is the key machine of modern farming, and the combine is an epitome of American agricultural mechanization, the modern farmer has numerous other machines which make work lighter and production greater. Many of these are still horse-drawn.

Corn planters were in use before 1860, but they left much to be desired. Corn can be cultivated efficiently by machine only if the rows are equidistant, and if the corn in the rows is spaced equally. This means that the seeds

must be dropped with mathematical precision. The old corn planters could not do this, so the checkrow planter was evolved for exactly this need. Soon after, other corn machines, cultivators, cutters, binders, huskers, and shellers appeared; so that by the first part of the twentieth century, corn farming was thoroughly mechanized.

There are still many cornfields all over America which are planted and harvested by hand in the fashion of three hundred years ago; but on the great corn farms mechanization is vital. Comparison statistics show the following: in 1855 it took 38 hours and 45 minutes of labor to produce about 40 bushels of corn on an acre; in 1930 it took five hours and 21 minutes to produce 50 bushels on an acre. [4]

Similar improvements with other crops were accomplished through machines. Hay is an example. In 1860 it took 35 hours and 30 minutes of work to cut, dry, and bale a ton of timothy hay by the methods then used. In 1931 the same ton required but four hours and eight minutes, [5] thanks to tractor-drawn mowers, tedders and rakes, motorized baling presses, and motor-truck haulage.

Basic tools were, of course, similarly improved. The sulky plow first appeared about 1865 and was soon followed by the disc plow and then the great gang plows. Other machines to be mentioned in passing are spring-toothed harrows, manure spreaders, potato diggers, feed choppers, silage choppers and blowers, ditch diggers, tile layers, milkers, coolers, and quick-freezers.

The Labor Problem

All in all, farmers have something like two billions of dollars invested in machines—an investment which must

be constantly renewed, for motors wear out, many machine parts are broken in use, and few farmers take adequate care of their tools. But while farming is thus "capitalistic," in the sense that both tools and the land itself now require money for purchase and money for maintenance, the really serious problem arising from mechanization is that of *labor*.

In colonial times and for about as long as the frontier endured, as well as for the period while industry was expanding, labor was in a chronic condition of shortage. Thanks to the machine, in normal times the situation is now reversed. We have 130,000,000 mouths of our own to feed three times a day, and many millions more in less fortunate sections of the world. During times of financial storm, millions of us go back home to be supported by relatives who have remained on the soil. But because machines help farmers produce more and more per capita, we need fewer and fewer farmers. There are other points involved, such as improved culture through the education of farmers in scientific methods. But it is fundamentally the multiplication of the farmer's strength by machines that is responsible for the comparatively subordinate condition of farmers numerically.

The Cotton Dilemma

An example of this economic problem caused by mechanization is the South. So far, mechanization in cotton raising and in other phases of Dixie farming has not kept pace with that in the wheatlands and cornfields. Tobacco, especially, is still much of a hand crop. Tobacco seed is very fine, and the plants are delicate. Picking and cultivation must necessarily be so careful and curing so much a

matter for judgment that machines are not of much value.

Cotton farming has been (until recently at least) somewhat similar. Machines can be used to plough and to fertilize and, to a degree, to cultivate—but the picking of cotton has been the province of human hands. Many thousands of Americans, mostly Negroes, still depend upon cotton picking for their living.

Now, a new machine, the cotton picker, threatens to overturn cotton farming, just as the cotton gin once did. Down South, "the whole social, political, and economic structure . . . still rests upon a tripod, whose three legs are the Negro, the mule, and the plow." [6] If the cotton picker proves out in practice, this tripod will be upset. A new era may begin, bringing, for a time, prosperity for a few and calamity for many. The whole history of the South lies behind this statement. Recent attempts at diversification may ameliorate threats of a cotton revolution, but the lives and destinies of most inhabitants of Dixie still hang upon employment provided by cotton.

The problem of the Negro inhabitants, which existed before the Civil War, was not solved by abolition of slavery. The cotton farmer before the war had fed, clothed, and lodged his slaves. After abolition the pattern changed. Abolition freed the planter of direct responsibility. Instead of being constantly concerned with supporting the hands, he changed over to a nominal wage system. Once a year, the cost of the Negro's effort to keep body and soul together was balanced off against his share in the year's crop. Call the system what we may—chattel slavery, tenancy, or share-cropping—the end result is the same. At the end of each year, the Negro drudge and the poor white laborer owe the proprietor of the land culti-

A New Machine   *Courtesy International Harvester Company*

The cotton picker may be an atomic bomb
to the labor situation in the South

vated somewhat more than they owed twelve months earlier. They sink further and further into debt. The situation is serious, for about sixty-eight per cent of Southern farmers are tenants.[7] The cotton farmer and the cotton laborer both suffer from this pitiful situation. Cotton is seldom grown efficiently under these conditions; the crop is poor and the land is abused.

The average cotton picker works usually for fifteen days a month during the three months of the harvest season and picks but a hundred pounds a day. This means but three bales a year for the average worker; and with cotton prices what they are, this inevitably means for the 1,192,-195 persons so employed an annual income so close to starvation that it is a miracle things today are no worse than they are.[8]

The cotton picker machine will mean efficient harvesting and, indirectly, prosperous cotton farming. But what will happen to the pickers? Where will they find work for their hands? This picking machine has been a long time in the making. More than eight hundred patents for such a device are on record already. Millions of dollars have been spent in attempts to develop a practical machine. Two brothers, John R. and Mack D. Rust, Texas cotton planters, seem finally to have developed a practical picker. It is reported to be superior to all other machines and is undoubtedly far better than were the first reapers, for example, in the wheat fields.

According to descriptions, the Rust picker, which selects only ripe bolls and passes over green bolls without injuring them (a correction of the common fault in other pickers) picks as much cotton in an hour as a good worker does during a whole season. The picker is tractor drawn

and goes back and forth over the fields in rotation as many times as the slowly ripening crop demands.

It is, essentially, an endless belt on wheels—something like a cotton gin which goes into the fields. Hundreds of wire spindles on the belt enter the ripe bolls, pull the cotton fibres free, and deliver them to a suction fan. This fan, in turn, picks the lint off the belt and packs it in bags.

Increased Production

It is often asserted that mechanization has ended the farmer's drudgery. This is not true. Farming, a lonesome profession, will always involve drudgery, for it must include a monotonous repetition of endless tasks. But mechanization has multiplied production by replacing the farmer's puny strength with motor-powered tools; and it has ended the problem of a labor shortage, creating in its stead, unemployment. Society will have to organize itself to provide jobs and living income for the farm hands made idle by machines.

[1] Bogart, E. L. *Economic History.* New York. 1935
[2] *Hand Labor Statistics, United States Commissioner of Labor.* Washington. 1898
[3] *Report of L. H. Guthals, Elmo, Kansas.* Both quoted by *Centennial Booklet of International Harvester Co.* Chicago. 1931
[4,5] *McCormick Centennial material.* International Harvester Co. Chicago. 1931
[6,7] Carlson, Oliver. *The Revolution in Cotton. American Mercury.* Feb. 1935
[8] Prof. Fletcher Green, University of North Carolina, at Harvard University, 1944-1945

CHAPTER XX

THE TIN CAN

EVERYWHERE GI Joe and Jane of the American Army have gone, and everywhere lend-lease has penetrated (and both include just about all the world), they have taken the American tin can. Although made not of tin but of steel, and though not really a can but a canister, the "tin can" is one of the greatest conveniences of modern times. It has not only greatly aided housekeeping, it has transformed agriculture.

Formerly, sales of perishable foods were limited to the few weeks in which the foods matured and to the local areas in which they could be distributed. Production was necessarily curtailed. Today, with almost every eatable preserved indefinitely inside steel shells, and with consumption made possible throughout the year and over areas as wide as the planet itself, the farmer has the world for his market.

Formerly, crops had to be dumped for sale in the short period of their maturity. This meant a temporary glut of the market for many things—and consequent low prices for the farmer. Now, to an extent, the canners absorb excess produce; and while prices are not always profitable for the farmer, at least they are somewhat stabilized. Furthermore, canners have striven not only to improve their techniques and to improve farm crops, they have encouraged breeders of tomatoes, peas, corn, and beans, for

example, so that varieties with qualities particularly adapted to canning might be obtained.

Similarly, the canners have encouraged plant pathologists and entomologists to fight diseases and pests. They have contracted with farmers, paid prices fixed in advance, and often have financed operations. In return, the farmer has had to farm with modern tools and methods. Thus the tin can has improved both the farmers' products and his methods, and has provided him with more stable prices and wider markets.

Preserving of Food

Theoretically, preserving of food is based upon preventing the bacteria that cause food decay from accomplishing their destruction. The growth of bacteria may be checked by various means.

Commonest is the employment of cold, which simply prevents these organisms from multiplying. Almost no bacteria grow under 32 degrees; and few develop under temperatures of 45 degrees. Thus the common household refrigerator serves its purpose; and the great cold storage plants keep large quantities of food from spoiling until the market can absorb them. The recently developed "quick-freeze" system and the new "frozen-food lockers" for home and community use are the latest improvements of the use of cold.

A second method of food preservation is to change the product itself so that bacteria will not develop in it for limited periods of time. Drying, salting, smoking, and fermenting are such familiar practices. Drying concentrates fruit acids, salts, and sugars by the evaporation of water, so that the normal bacteria do not grow. Salting, by ab-

sorbing water, has somewhat the same effect. Smoking (fish, hams, and bacon are examples) impregnates tissue with substances allied to carbolic acid, which destroys many species of bacteria.[1] Fermentation employs special bacteria to change sugars and starches to alcohols and acids. These destroy germs, improve the taste, and preserve the materials for long periods.

These are all old forms of food preservation—as old as agriculture itself. More important and more recent is the use of heat. Heat kills bacteria; and the foods, made sterile by heating, are protected from re-infection from bacteria by being tightly sealed in containers. Essentially, the process consists of "packing" foods in cans or jars and heating them until sterile. The process is the same, whether done in the farmhouse kitchen or in the huge factories of a packing corporation.

Today (pre-war figures are all that are available) the average value of commercially packed foods in America is about $875,000,000.[2] The needs of war times have probably greatly increased the figure. Behind this triumph is a long series of efforts by men in many lands. Back in 1795 the French government offered a prize of 12,000 francs to anyone who could devise a method of preserving foods so they would be wholesome for use by the French Navy. Navy food consisted in the main of hardtack and salt meat, and crews suffered greatly from food-deficiency diseases, such as scurvy. A Paris confectioner, Nicholas Appert, worked on the problem for ten years and, in 1809, was finally awarded the prize. He packed foods in glass bottles, sealed them with hand-cut corks, wired the stoppers fast—and then sterilized them by immersion in boiling water.[3]

This was simply "trial and error" experimentation; and it was not until 1860, when Pasteur finally demonstrated scientifically the role of bacteria, yeasts, and moulds in food spoilage, that the canning industry really knew what it was doing. Years passed, even after Pasteur, before canners really applied scientific principles, although in Boston William L. Underwood worked out the basic practical methods. He demonstrated, for example, that the spoilage of canned corn was due to imperfect sterilization at the time of canning.[4]

Later, the United States Department of Agriculture entered the field with a program of organized research; and in 1913 the canners themselves enlisted the direct aid of scientists. That year the National Canners Association opened its Washington laboratory, and, subsequently, establishments in Seattle and San Francisco. Thus, by the time the First World War created a need for vast quantities of canned goods, the industry was ready to supply them. It had become a progressive business, one that based its production on test tubes and microscopes.

In the beginning, although France initiated canning, British merchants soon took the world leadership with the founding of several famous firms. One of the great contributions of Britain was the substitution of the English tea canister for the glass jars and bottles of the French. Glass was then blown by hand and was very expensive, while the tin canister, although also handmade, was comparatively cheap. Just how the name tin canister was shortened to "tin can" is not known, but it is suggested that American bookkeepers, making many entries in their ledgers of shipments, abbreviated tin canister to tin can.[5]

America was not long behind Britain. Ezra Daggett

and Thomas Kensett, New York merchants, by 1819 were packing salmon, lobsters, and oysters. In Boston, by 1812 William L. Underwood was experimenting with fruits, pickles, and condiments in glass jars. Kensett was awarded the first American canning patent; and his document is dated 1825.[6]

During the thirties there was little progress in canning; but in the forties, in Maine, Isaac Winslow, starting his work in 1839, devoted himself to experimenting with canned corn. Salmon and lobsters were by then being packed in Maine and in New Brunswick. Oyster packing began at Baltimore. Crosby in Pennsylvania started canning tomatoes. The fifties brought Winslow's patent for the steam packing of corn; while Gail Borden, originator of a method of condensing milk, established the first condensed milk factory in America.

Despite the Civil War (perhaps because of it) during the sixties, canning boomed. Commercial packing began in Ohio, Indiana, and Illinois; while salmon packing started on the Sacramento River in 1864 and on the Columbia River in 1866. The following years brought great progress. Iowa began the packing of vegetables about 1870, Chicago started packing meats in 1872; shrimps were first commercially canned at New Orleans in 1875; and canned sardines appeared in Maine factories at about the same time.

In Alaska, salmon packing began in 1878 on Prince of Wales Island. The first peas were tinned in Wisconsin in 1881, and Hawaii packed its first pineapple in 1891, while tuna fish were tinned in California in 1907.

Since the turn of the century there have been few limits to the growth of canning. Almost everything is now

packed. The development of machinery has made it possible to preserve things which formerly cost too much to process. Grapefruit is an example. At first the fruit rotted on the ground, because the hand labor required to separate the pulp from the rind was too costly. Then a machine was developed to do the work, and now canned grapefruit segments are even more popular than the juice itself. Americans took to vitamins in the thirties; and fruit juices were one excellent source of these mysterious substances.

The size of present-day (before the Second World War) canning can be measured not only by the billion-dollar value annually, but also by the number of cans packed each year. Canners measure their output by the case, whether the case holds six large cans or ninety-six small ones.

However, the cubic contents of the cases are about uniform, so that the packing-case measurement is adequate. Here is the recent average annual pack: fruits, 50,000,000 cases; vegetables, 165,000,000; milk products, 40,000,000; meat and meat products, 12,000,000; and seafoods, 17,000,000 cases.[7]

Most canning establishments are small; sixty per cent of them have an annual average pack of less than $100,000 in value.[8] These plants are widely distributed, for it is one advantage of canning that factories can be built where the foods are most abundantly produced. There are such factories in forty-five States, as well as in Alaska, Hawaii, and Puerto Rico. Vegetable packing is most widely distributed. Beans are canned in forty States, tomatoes in thirty-seven, corn in twenty-nine, and peas in twenty-seven. Fruit canning leads on the Pacific Coast, shrimp

packing is confined to the Gulf Coast, and meat canning centers in the Middle West.[9]

The Can Itself

Much of this progress has been made possible by the tin can itself. Originally the cans were made by hand, and only an industrious man could produce as many as sixty in a day. In contrast, modern machines make perfect cans at the rate of 300 a minute.[10]

The can was a serious problem. It had to be airtight permanently. It had to be made of a heat conducting material so that its contents would sterilize quickly. It had to be light in weight for shipping and yet strong enough to withstand rough handling, and it had to be cheap for volume production. All of these qualities are to be found in steel.

One other quality was necessary. The steel had to be protected against rusting and against reaction with foods. Tin-plating was the answer. Tin is one of the oldest of metals, and tin-plating is not new. It was common in Bohemia, for example, in the thirteenth century,[11] and England had a tin-plate industry well established by 1655.[12]

But neither tin nor tin-plating was of much importance until about 1840, when British merchants began to use tin canisters for food packing. The tea canisters they employed had been developed previously, for tea is a delicate thing and must be kept tightly sealed against the air. Then when food packing became a mass production industry, the problem was to develop tin-plate production accordingly.

Here in America, we accomplished a great deal in tin-plate manufacture, although, as we discovered after Pearl

Harbor, we have no tin of our own of any importance. Cut off from our main source of large supply, Malaya, we turned to Bolivia and to the desperate salvaging of used tin cans. Also we developed a much more efficient plating method. This is a story of technical triumph to be told after peace returns.

As for steel, we had no trouble in meeting our needs, for we are masters of steel. We annually used (before the Second World War) 1,150,000 tons of tin plate in making tin cans. This is about five billion square feet of tin plate; and it consumes some 1,692,000 tons of steel. To make this, we use 1,880,000 tons of pig iron, which require 3,420,-000 tons of 55 per cent ore, 2,820,000 tons of coal plus another 1,600,000 tons of coal in subsequent heating.[13]

Formerly, quantities of solder were needed to seal the tin cans tightly; but the recent perfection of machines which cut, roll, fold, and lock the three pieces of can together have greatly reduced the amount of solder required. A recent improvement in tin cans (as a result of the war) is the replacement of tin by various plastic enamels and coatings. Wartime needs have stimulated the packing industry tremendously, not only in volume of production, but in techniques and practices.

As a result, today the packing of foods has become both highly efficient and economical. It will continue to be a vital part of most American daily lives. When rationing is nothing but a memory, we shall still benefit by at least this detail of wartime urgency.

[1, 2] Taylor, S. F. *The World of Science*. London. 1937
[3, 4] National Canners Association. *The Story of the Canning Industry*. Washington. 1939
[5, 6] National Canners Association. *History of Canning*. Washington. 1939
[7, 8, 9] National Canners Association. *The Canning Industry*. Washington. 1939
[10, 11, 12, 13] National Canners Association. *The Story of the Tin Can*. Washington. 1936

PART V

TODAY AND TOMORROW

CHAPTER XXI

PAYMENT DUE

IMAGINE you have a supertelevision radio with a space-time attachment. Set your dials to May 11, 1934, and for almost any spot in Kansas near the Colorado line. The picture develops a black angry cloud sweeping towards you over the brown, level plains. The soil itself is gaping open with drought; and you see only a few scattered, paint-blistered shacks that discouraged farmers call home. This cloud racing out of the West is a dust storm caused by overcropping; by abuse of the soil. It rages for hours. Stricken humans dig their way out through the dunes piled against their houses; with handkerchiefs tied over their faces like gas masks, for the air is still heavy with choking dust, they go about counting their losses.

The familiar face of things has been forever altered. Where the morning sun shone on green winter wheat that promised security for the farmer and his family for a year to come, nothing shows in the wan afternoon light but a desert of gray sand. It is lifeless stuff, heaped everywhere in the lee of houses, barns, banks, and fences. Roadside ditches are filled level with what were highways. Desolation has swirled over the prairie.

Not once has this dusty catastrophe struck—but several times. The heart of America, a multitude of farms, once prosperous, became our Dust Bowl. As the Great Drought endured, the winds lifted up the fertile topsoil and

freighted it eastward. Across the Mississippi and over the Appalachians the dust was taken, sometimes even out over the Atlantic Ocean.

The dust storms are Item One on the bill Nature is presenting to America for payment because of the abuse of the soil. Cattlemen say: "We told you so! The prairie sod should never have been broken to farms!"

Farmers blame it to the drought, that made the soil stone hard; that made it necessary to send merciful bullets into the brains of cattle, starved to the point of death in a hopeless quest for water and grass.

"It will rain again; just wait," insisted the farmers.

It did rain, finally. After enormous losses the Dust Bowl grew green again. Once more crops were good and cattle plump; but scientists know it will be dry again before long. Meteorologists recognize that the weather runs its mysterious way in alternate cycles of wet and dry. Some set the cycle period at seven years. Others, thinking of sunspots and the relation of those solar hurricanes to the volume of radiation the earth receives, set the cycles at the sunspot rhythm of 11½ years, or such multiples as 23 and 46. The basic fact is, there are wet periods and dry periods.

The welfare of our Dust Bowl States may expand and contract with the weather cycles. It is probable that areas of the once sodded plains should not have had their armor of sod plowed under. As long as the grass endured, there was no trouble. The grass stored the rain; and then, in time of drought, anchored the soil against the winds.

But the grass is gone; and the soil is defenceless against the gale. The soil is fertile. The long and level acres are ideal for efficient machine cultivation. All that is needed

FATAL WASTE OF LAND
Water erosion caused this once prosperous farm
to be abandoned

is water. But without water, the black blizzards and their devastation seem inevitable.

Something may yet be done to reclaim the Dust Bowl sections. Massive windbreaks of trees have been planted to halt the fury of the winds. New techniques of farming have been developed to make the most of the rain and the winter snow. But the land has been too thoroughly exploited—and Nature always exacts the price for any abuse.

Item Two

Now shift the dials of our superspace and supertime machine again. Come East to the thin and ragged cutover forests of the watersheds of the Ohio-Mississippi rivers. Set the time for almost any winter or early spring period, say late January of 1937.

Up from the Gulf of Mexico a warm air mass, saturated with water lifted from the steamy tropical sea, has been pouring northeastward. Meanwhile, out of the Arctic colds, coming down from Alaska along the mountains into the Canadian plains and then over the Great Lakes, another air mass has moved. It is cold, dry, and very heavy.

Over the western slopes of the Appalachians, over Pennsylvania, Ohio, Indiana, West Virginia, and Kentucky, the two air masses come into conflict—like two armies meeting. The "front" between them becomes a storm. Winds roar, and out of the tropical air-mass the water is emptied. Hour after hour the rain pours down— two inches, three inches, four, five, and six. Billions of tons of water smash down into the basins of the Ohio and the Mississippi.

Had the forests been unspoiled and so had absorbed the water; had farms been cultivated so as to catch and impound it; had the multitude of little streams in the hills been provided with catch-basins and storage ponds, nothing very detrimental would have happened. But the forests had been thinned and their floors robbed of water-drinking ability. The farms and their furrows invited destruction, and the brooks had no protective dams. So the rain drained right through the forests. On each farm the furrows ran downhill. The rain tore through the fields in many streams. All this drainage from the hillsides roared into the brooks. These, rising till they burst their ice, poured into the rivers, which in turn delivered their burdens into the Ohio and the Mississippi.

Those mighty streams can carry water more than 2,000 miles back to the Gulf only so fast and no faster. So, as the yeasty flood from the hills continued to rise, the rivers mounted higher and higher and still higher. This in turn caused the tributary streams to be dammed by walls of water at their mouths; and they turned their waters back into the hills. A flood had come into being, burying cities, towns, and villages under yellow tides.

Our time machine shows us men working at dikes without rest; while other multitudes of frightened men, women, and children struggle to save themselves. Feverishly they run towards higher ground, perhaps in trucks laden with a few precious things, perhaps in leaking rowboats. Most have not even a loaf of bread or a jug of safe water with them. And downstream drift millions of dollars of property, in houses and furnishings, livestock, and human bodies.

Next, our time-and-space screen shows America rising

as a unit to help. Mercy mobilized comes over the mountains from the East. Coast guard motorboats, hauled by truck even from as far as Boston, chug over the floodwaters carrying food, drugs, clothing, and fuel to shivering and hungry refugee camps. A little later we watch the water ebb behind the flood crest as it runs south. Cold returns, changes the flood water to ice, and adds fresh misery to homeless thousands. Back to their farms, their factories, and their homes, finally go the farmers, mechanics, and clerks.

Being Americans and as such incurable optimists, the stricken people go to work. Reconstruction follows the flood right down to the rivers' edges once again. Millions of dollars are borrowed and spent to plough roads clear from sand, to rid the farm lands of debris, to rebuild collapsed houses, and to fill in sections washed out of river banks. Millions more are borrowed to build more flood walls, more dikes, more storage basins, more dams—more of the little and futile things that we hope will tame the next flood. Homes are rebuilt, new livestock purchased, and the farmer plans again to plant his crops. Broken families strive to forget empty chairs and drive to town to arrange for an increase on the farm mortgage to "tide us over till harvest time."

Humans have suffered, have lost in many instances the savings of years. This means little comparatively to the great loss our America has sustained. Nothing can replace in human time the basic substance of the nation that the flood has taken, and that floods great and small take each year.

With each flood America loses some more of its most important wealth—the soil. Multitudes of tons of this

precious stuff have been lost. Torn by racing waters from
the hills, washed away from the leveler farm fields, it now
chokes the beds of the rivers and slowly drifts downstream
to pour into the deeps of the ocean.

The vast, marshy delta of the Mississippi, only a small
fraction of which is above water, is one example of this
wealth we have lost. Every grain of that delta—and of
the banks and shoals at the mouth of every American river
—is mute testimony to this Second Item which Nature
presents to America for payment because of our abuse of
the land. Something had to be done about it. And we are
doing something—now that it is almost too late!

Item Three

Jobless men stand in long lines, waiting for bread and
soup—the gift of a city to its unfortunates. Down the same
street are "Welfare Department" offices where, all day
long, people a little more fortunate come and wait their
turn. These are mostly women and children. Each appli-
cant leaves the interview with a card that entitles the
holder to some food, some shelter, some clothing, some
medical aid. These are the items of public charity,
financed by city, State, and nation, to keep families together. The family is the unit of the nation. The family
must be preserved; and accordingly, charity is doled out,
mechanically.

Of course, some jobs have been provided in times of
greatest emergency, such as WPA jobs in the late thirties.
Some are "made" jobs—jobs for the most part wastefully
managed and poorly planned. But they are jobs, and the
system does preserve a measure of self-respect.

Such is another item on the bill Nature has presented

DESTRUCTION OF NATURAL RESOURCES
Fire and flood ruined this once fertile valley

to America, the land with millions of farms, factories, and shops. Because of our abuse of our resources, this is the charity we often find necessary. It is charity supported by heavy taxes while the land is abused, and machines stand idle.

Item Four

Shift the dials of our television set once more to a farm that is comparatively prosperous. The picture is one very easily over-sentimentalized. Many Americans think of farming in Currier-and-Ives-print terms. It is true that almost any farm family, if the men work hard and the women are good managers, has enough to eat and enough fuel to burn. We see cellars and pantries well-filled and the barns and fields well-stocked.

Actually, if we look a little closer, we can see the bitter pattern of poverty showing through almost everywhere. Half of the farm families in the United States, (except during the desperate years of the depression) receive gross incomes of less than $1,000 annually.[1]

Of course, most of us farm not for profit alone. Essentially, farming is a way of life which offers a multitude of values equally as desirable as urban amenities purchased through regular wages. But many farm families seldom have money enough for even the materials they need, let alone the luxuries they would like to enjoy. Education, recreation, health, all suffer for this reason.

America has a high standard of living, but much of America's enjoyment of its place in the sun is beyond the reach of the average farmer. His place is on the outer fringe. His cotton cannot be sold for prices high enough to make the culture pay its own way. His corn and wheat

often bring so little profit that they are hardly worth the cost of harvesting. Every now and then, while millions of American men, women, and children escape starvation only by charity; while other hosts suffer for lack of food, fuel, and clothing—much of the produce of the good earth goes to waste.

Efforts have been and are being made to remedy the situation. Before the war, economists sought, for example, to improve things by limiting production. Farmers, who could not believe it true until checks arrived, were paid *not* to raise pigs; *not* to grow corn; and to let some of their land lie idle. Many were the schemes tried—even to the free distribution of surplus food by the welfare stamp system. Financed by tax money, the thirties were marked by a series of experiments, noble in purpose but at times unfortunate in execution.

Such is another item on the bill Nature has presented for payment—this item for our failure to use the bounty of the soil properly.

Accumulated Evils

We could continue this unhappy series of television scenes for some time. We could look in at share-croppers. We could ride the roads with the migrant workers. We could hear the hammer of the auctioneer selling off farms and homes for mortgage failure. We could see hosts of American men and women, desperate for money, willing to do anything that they might live and meet their obligations and responsibilities.

Whatever the effects, the causes are now clear. For three centuries we were so wealthy in resources that we could exploit our land as rapaciously as we wished.

Butchered forests, over-cropped fields, haphazard distribution, and ruthless banking accumulated evils until America was settled, until a frontier was reached. These extravagances then descended upon us like locusts, riding out of the West on the winds of dust storms and coming down every stream upon the silty waters of the floods.

Outraged Nature is presenting her bill. Payment is due —overdue.

The recent appointment by President Truman of Clinton P. Anderson of Albuquerque, New Mexico, as Secretary of Agriculture to succeed Claude R. Wickard, may have great significance. Mr. Anderson is a sometime chairman of the Food Committee of the House of Representatives. As such he was responsible for that committee's nine-point program for the alleviation of the food crisis. This appointment, following V-E Day, can be regarded as exemplifying a change in policy from that followed by the Roosevelt administration.

The committee's report called for a revision of price policies to permit the profitable processing and distribution of meat at all stages of its production, a top priority for basic food production through 1947, and the giving of authority to one man and holding him responsible.

This program, among other aspects, evidently entails a realization of the error of supporting prices at one end of a food production program and of controlling prices at the other. It also entails an admission that the curtailment of production—as of hogs for one example—was a mistake. And, finally, it entails the recognition that divided authority cannot be efficient.

[1] Wend, Milton. *How to Live in the Country.* New York. 1944

CHAPTER XXII

CONSERVATION AND REGIMENTATION

MARCH, 1933, was a gloomy time for the whole nation, whose banks were closed, industry palsied, and optimism for once shattered. The rain drizzled down upon thousands of people massed before the Capitol watching a certain man standing in the downpour, taking his oath of office as the President of the United States.

Through microphones his words were picked up by radios in nearly every home in the United States. His heartening message created enthusiasm. At the time, people clung almost fanatically to anything he had to suggest. Economic conditions were so bad that our entire citizenry, from the boards of great corporations down to the share-croppers, were ready to lean upon any shoulder of authority that offered itself. Even the policy of *spending* our way out of the Great Depression seemed a good idea—then.

Before long, of course, opposition to the Roosevelt Administration appeared; and soon a somewhat vigorous revolt was organized. However, the policies and the ideas of the Administration had gained a sufficiently firm hold upon a large enough number of people to keep the so-called New Deal in office.

In 1936, in 1940, and in 1944, tradition was shattered, and the President was re-elected. Nothing, it seemed,

could halt him in his innovations. Even the Supreme Court's few adverse decisions, as in the NRA, did not stop, but only shifted the Administration in its course.

Among the countless applications of the Administration's ideas to the betterment of conditions and to the improvement of the American way of life, the vexed problems of agriculture received (for once) plenty of attention. Vigorous and immediate action was necessary in many details of farm life as well as in the distribution of farm products. Such attention was bestowed. This book cannot pass judgment upon the faults and virtues of the New Deal's drive to improve the lot of the farmer. No man contemporary with great events is capable of making worthwhile conclusions. The future alone can do that.

For this reason, a brief chronology of the outstanding events—particularly of the various acts by and through which our Government responded to the needs of the farmer—is appended. The record of the legislation is impressive and speaks for itself. Thus, in the limits of this chapter, an attempt is made to provide merely the background of agricultural conditions in the past fifteen years —together with such opinions as seem pertinent.

The Federal Farm Board

In March of 1933 the farmer's plight was little short of desperate. In the Autumn of 1929 cash farm income was $1,300,000,000. In the Autumn of 1933 it had collapsed to about $300,000,000.[1]

The Administration of President Hoover had attempted to halt this decline of prices. One of the planks of the Republican Party platform for the election of 1928

had promised farm relief. So Congress on June 15, 1929, had created the Federal Farm Board.

Given $200,000,000—then considered a huge sum—this Board had authority to control the marketing of farm products in interstate and foreign commerce. In addition it had the power to acquire surplus crops, to store them, and to set up various organizations for the purpose of stabilizing prices and marketing.

Alexander Legge of the International Harvester Company was made chairman; and various agricultural personages, such as growers of wheat, cotton, tobacco, livestock, dairy products, and fruit, were represented on the board.

One of the first actions was typical—the establishment of the Grain Stabilization Agency. By the middle of 1931 there were 250,000,000 bushels of wheat in storage, held from a saturated market.

During 1932 Congress began to distribute some of this wheat among suffering citizens; but the policy was rendered ineffective because many persons believed it would not do for the Government to become paternalistic. They seemed to think it better to have citizens go hungry than for the Government to feed them wheat which otherwise would go to waste!

While the wheat was being purchased, the Board's Cotton Stabilization Corporation was purchasing and storing cotton. Soon some million bales (about 500,000,000 pounds) were so taken from the market. But, as with wheat, the decline in cotton prices was not materially halted, although how much worse things might have been without this Government purchasing, no one can say. The Board finally suggested that farmers should voluntarily

SAVING THE SOIL
Wisconsin soil conservation by contour planting
Prize photograph by James N. Meyer

curtail production; but nothing definite was ever accomplished at that time.

All in all, by 1933, when the Farm Board was wound up, and the salaries of its officers were removed from the Federal payroll, it is likely that it had cost the taxpayers $184,000,000.[2] All over the country, farmers were near that point of desperation which causes serious trouble. Farm-mortgage foreclosures were increasing startlingly; and groups of farmers joined together to check the loss of their homes, under such names as the "Farmers' Holiday Association."

In April of 1932, in a single day of misery, twenty-five per cent of all Mississippi's farm lands were sold by the sheriff![3] Iowa, as in the days of a century before, was active in resisting due legal processes. Although only one actual case of assault upon a peace officer is recorded,[4] the farmers did exert considerable pressure to save their farms. For example, on the hour assigned for a foreclosure sale, neighbors crowded about, silenced or intimidated serious bidders, purchased the farm and its equipment for a few dollars, and then handed back the debt-free farm to its rightful owner!

It is to the everlasting credit of the American farmer that there was very little trouble. In other days, and even in other countries today, the story could have been one of revolution. American roads were wet with milk from trucks overturned by strikers—but the same roads might have been wet with human blood.

The Boom of the Twenties

We were trying to run our farms upon a system that had just naturally "growed up of itself." Before the First

World War, things had been well enough, save for depression after the Civil War. The need then had been for production and ever more production. The idea that there could be a serious and long-continued farm overproduction had never occurred to anyone of prominence. With the whole civilized world reasonably prosperous, foreign trade could usually be relied upon as a market for relieving any considerable food surplus at reasonable prices.

But 1914-1918 changed that. The economic background is complicated. Any oversimplification in relating conditions means inadequate statement. But in general, while industry thrived and the stock market boomed, in the era of "Coolidge confidence," the farmer started slipping and was soon on the toboggan economically. No longer could he solve his ills by the simple experiment of producing more. Thanks to his machines, he was producing much too much!

Then the comparative collapse of foreign markets for farm products arrived, to aggravate things. From a debtor nation, America had become a creditor nation. This in spite of our not being able to collect even the interest on our war loans, not to mention the principal (Finland excepted). Other nations could not pay us money for our wheat and meat, because they had no money. We could not accept their goods in barter, both because of our high tariff and because we had plenty of goods being produced from our own factories and mills.

The farmer was injured doubly. He could not sell all he produced, and prices fell lower and lower for what he could sell. At the same time, prices for the things he had to buy began to soar. So the stage was set for the Crash of 1929 and the slow ebbing of the economic tide

into 1933. Just as the stars can be seen only when the sun has set, so the darkness of the Great Depression brought out the flaws in American farming as well as the economic sins of the nation as a whole.

Secretary of Agriculture Wallace

When President Roosevelt began his long term of office, the farmers faced mountainous surpluses with no buyers in prospect. Just as bread lines grew longer in the cities, so did these surpluses increase. And this despite the fact that the prices of farm products were but half of what they had been in 1916.

The appointment of Henry A. Wallace of Iowa as the Secretary of Agriculture marked the determination of the Administration to take action. Things at once began to happen.

To solve the immediate problems of farm surpluses and farm income, the Farm Relief Act was passed on May 12, 1933. This was a revolutionary measure. It shifted policy from the traditional encouragement of production to the opposite pole of control of production. The idea was to reduce the surplus and to increase prices by cutting down production. The new item in the plan was that the farmers were to be paid for their sacrifices.

This Act and related legislation also sought "to halt overproduction and waste, to bring about orderly marketing, to reduce tariff barriers, to regain lost foreign markets, to expand domestic markets by distributing surplus farm products to hungry people in the cities, and by definite steps to improve farm income and thus, farm purchasing power." [5]

The real meat of the proposal, however, was the cur-

tailment of production by outright payments to farmers, to reimburse them for lost crops.

Wheat will serve as an example. On July 9, 1933, a processing tax of 30 cents was put upon each bushel used domestically. The tax was collected from the original processor, the miller, and passed down the line to the ultimate consumer, who paid the bill. This was a direct boost in the price of bread; but actually it was only an application to farm products of the tariff principle which already had been employed for a century for the benefit of industrialists.

The proceeds from this tax were to be divided among wheat farmers in proportion to the amount by which they cut production the following season. One theoretical trouble with the idea was that as soon as wheat prices rose to profitable levels, the farmers would desert crop limitation so as to cash in on the market.

The real trouble with the idea was, of course, the fact that the Supreme Court found it unconstitutional. But the Act had worked; and the Government paid millions to the farmers who had joined the plan. The processors of wheat, tobacco, cotton, and the rest had of course collected many millions of dollars. This money the Government proceeded to collect by means of a division of the Income Tax organization known as the Bureau of Unjust Enrichment. Ultimately, most of the process tax money found its way into the national coffers.

Radical as this policy was, it was still concerned with production. So the next step of the Administration was towards the control of distribution. The process was meagre, but in its total, much of the surplus food was finally moved.

The job was begun with pigs. To relieve the glut of pork, the Government had purchased some 6,000,000 pigs, which were made into pork and given to persons on charity lists and work-relief payrolls. The pork was reported to be of inferior quality, for it was surplus production sold to the Government to get it out of the way. But it was something for unfortunate people, who otherwise might have had no meat.

In addition to pork, other surplus commodities were purchased—fish, fowl, flesh, as well as oranges from Florida, potatoes from Maine, and flour from Minneapolis.

This gave farmers as a group a little lift, for it somewhat reduced surpluses. Then the drought of 1934 and the second drought of 1935 enlisted Nature to end practically any major surplus. Farm income rose promptly, almost reaching $1,100,000,000 in the fall of 1936.[6] Finally, the farm problem was aided by the Second World War.

Conservation

The drought also helped, by means of the dust storms, to point out a second line of attack on farm trouble. Thus, to the efforts to control prices and production by what has been called regimentation, was added the determined drive for conservation.

It was abundantly clear that just as unrestrained production required a measure of control, so the free and easy exploitation of the land had to be tempered by the conservation of what we had left. Floods and drought, forest fires, and dust storms seem to have been necessary to compel the required development of public opinion. If so,

the price has been high, but perhaps it has been not altogether in vain.

There followed what seems to be a really profound alteration in our national habits. Americans began to listen. The day had ended when conservationists pleaded to indifferent ears for control over ruthless destruction. Much conservation legislation has been enacted to attempt to solve some of our land abuses. This does not include such things as the Tennessee Valley Authority, because the general economic phases of that plan are distinct from the purely agricultural.

"This legislation has resulted in widespread action; (1) to protect land against erosion, (2) to expand the use of soil-conserving and soil-building crops, (3) to shift land from unprofitable and undesirable uses to use for which it is better suited, (4) to conserve and make better use of forest and water resources, and (5) to study and treat watersheds to assist in flood control." [7]

Detailed legislation for this conservation activity and for the steps in the development of control of production and marketing appear in the previously mentioned appendix. Such items will include the Ever-Normal Granary Provision of the Agricultural Adjustment Act of 1938, explained by Secretary Wallace as follows: [8]

"It became evident that there was a real need for some orderly means of storing and withholding for market needed reserves of farm products. The effects of drought had also pointed to the need for an orderly storing and releasing of reserves to help stabilize market supplies and prices for the benefit of both consumers and producers. The Ever-Normal Granary provision . . . met this need."

CONSERVATION OF THE LAND
Lister ridges impound the winter range
on this Oklahoma farm

And the list of experiments and solutions could be continued right down to the crop insurance and flood control controversies of 1944 and 1945.

Trade

Meanwhile, there was still another field into which the Administration ventured in its efforts to help the farmer. This was the export trade. By 1938 world conditions indicated that further limitation of agricultural exports was likely. Said Mr. Wallace:[9]

"Barter agreements, export subsidies, and the underselling by foreign producers made possible by efforts to protect income of producers in this country began to put farmers at a disadvantage . . ."

Whatever the Administration might have been able to accomplish in this difficult field—difficult not only because of its complexity but because foreign nations are not subject to Congress—cannot now be known. The War arrived, Lend-Lease appeared, and farmers overnight gained the best market they have ever known.

The war's need for food was a national emergency, and it was an international crisis. The American farmer was handicapped by the draft for military needs and by the wholesale desertion of laborers, drawn like moths to the high-wage flame of war industries. He was limited by the almost total cessation of production of many items of farm tools and machinery. Yet he responded loyally.

If dawn to dark was not time enough, then the farmer hitched headlights to his tractor and kept on plowing, cultivating, and harvesting far into the night. But the weary men and women produced a volume of food in amounts that will stagger America when the figures are

released. The farm family earned every cent of what it received, and much more as well.

After the War

Mars has always had a way of solving difficulties by postponing them until after victory. Thus the aid of foreign trade as a means of stabilizing the American farm products market has not been solved by Lend-Lease. That problem will await us as soon as scarcity of goods comes to an end with the war.

And there still remain many of the old familiar problems, including that of tenant farmers. The Administration did begin to attack this problem in the late thirties. It was evident that things being tried for the farmer's benefit would be useless unless that farmer was enabled to retain ownership of his land.

As a background to this great problem, it is to be remembered that studies show an alarming increase in tenancy, desperate conditions among farm families ruined by the drought, very bad conditions among migratory farm laborers, and other evils. Clearly, if the land is to remain in the hands of small, independent proprietors, which is the traditional American way, then Governmental assistance is needed.

Already legislation has been enacted which authorizes rehabilitation loans and gives direct assistance to farmers and their families. Other legislation has been passed which helped tenants and migrants to become proprietors of their own farms, in the form of resettlement. But this legislation has been more or less halted by the Second World War.

During the past fifteen years the response of the Fed-

eral Government has been both varied and vast. The era has been called by many names, some not complimentary, but it has brought developments whose significance cannot now be judged fully.

Irrigation projects are but beginning, which have cost millions of dollars to place farmers on what had been desert lands. Mighty transformations of depressed sections, such as the Tennessee Valley Authority, are symbolic of a Government policy which was impossible even a generation ago.

The Government has not solved the farm problem. It is too complicated to be solved in a few years. After all, it has been three centuries in the making. But the Government has made a very good start in such things as protecting farm income, practicing real conservation, promoting the sensible use of the land, giving farmers a measure of security, establishing means of more efficient production, distribution and stabilization and, most important, demonstrating to the farmer that he is not always going to be the Forgotten Man.

[1] *Federal Reserve Charts*. Edition of 1943
[2,3,4] Shannon, Fred A. *Economic History*. New York. 1934
[5] Statement of Secretary of Agriculture Wallace, given to the author, November, 1939
[6] Federal Reserve Chart. *Op. cit.*
[7,8,9] Secretary of State Wallace. *Op. cit.*

CHAPTER XXIII

CHEMISTRY TAKES COMMAND

"THESE tomatoes were picked only an hour ago, sir," smiles the waiter in the dining room of a great liner three days at sea, a ship lunging eastward through a mid-Atlantic winter gale. And the fruit was picked only an hour before! Sheltered behind the chart house and just forward of the smoke-belching stacks is a greenhouse in which tomatoes are growing. In the warm, placid air, shut from the stinging snow of the storm, flowers are blooming, too—roses, lilies, and orchids.

There are other unusual greenhouses. One is on the roof of a skyscraper hotel in Manhattan. It is not a conservatory but a serious production plant, where tomatoes run up on trellises for fifteen and twenty feet, each vine heavy with fruit. Roses stand six feet tall, bearing crimson heads level with a man's eyes. Sweet peas swarm over their wires and reach for the roof. Gardenia bushes stand stiffly, their branches starred with creamy white blossoms. Seasons stop short at the glass panes; the year around, this greenhouse sends its fruits and flowers downstairs to serve the patrons of the hotel.

Another of these greenhouses is built almost underground, beyond the Arctic Circle, where the sun does not appear for months at a time; where the soil never thaws; and almost nothing green can grow. Snow banks the roof which is set just about level with the surface of the ground.

308

Overhead, windmills spin constantly in the gales driving down from the North Pole itself. Generators are thus spun to make the electricity which heats and lights the beds of green and growing things. There are strawberries turning red, lettuces crisp and green, pots of narcissi and of fragrant violets. This is the "farm" that provides vegetables, flowers, and fruits for Russian meteorologists, self-exiled scientists enduring the Arctic night to study and to observe the polar air masses so that weather forecasting may be improved everywhere in the world.

Three such greenhouses—one on an ocean liner, one in New York, and a third in the Arctic—they are widely separated, yet all are united by one fact. They are emancipated from the soil and from the weather!

Not a particle of soil ever enters these houses. The plants are grown in water. Supported by wires or with their roots thrust into cinders, each plant is fed by chemical solutions cunningly brewed by master scientists to give them every item they need. Bits of this salt and ounces of that salt, mixed and blended with more than a dozen other inorganic substances, replace the nourishment which plants usually extract from the soil. Thus soil has been eliminated; and with it, all the hosts of soil-born and soil-nurtured insects and diseases.

Electricity aids the sun, both for warmth and light necessary for the photo-processes that produce food and beauty out of air, water, and soil-salts. The atmosphere is taken in, warmed if too cold, filtered if need be, and drifted about the plants to meet their needs. Thus, weather stops short at the greenhouse door; and plants can be successfully grown anywhere, any time, with almost machine-like precision.[1]

This soilless, weatherless garden was merely in preliminary experimental stage at the opening of the Second World War. Even then, an American air line had established soilless garden tanks and frames on a desert island in the mid-Pacific. It was cheaper to grow fruits and vegetables in this new manner than to transport them there. This newest type of farming has a tremendous and brilliant future of its own—a vast, new scientific domain yet to be fully explored by the new "educated" farmer.

Colchicine

Step into any one of the many agricultural experimental laboratories of America, institutions supported by public funds or by private foundations. You might see an experimentator take in hand a bottle filled with a white and poisonous powder. The label reads "Colchicine." It is a product of the common autumn-flowering, crocus-like garden plant, *Colchicum*. For many years, an extract of this plant has served as a remedy for gout.

But this scientist is not thinking of human ills. He makes a delicately accurate solution of the powder. Colchicine is a tool he will use in order to reach into the inmost recesses of plant germ plasma. He will upset exquisitely fine chemical balances and thus create new plants —whether miracles or monstrosities.

The scientist will explain that colchicine is a specific intra-cellular poison which can bring about the normal separation of half-chromosomes during cellular division, while most other cellular processes are not affected. This means that the normal sexual reproduction of a plant (the formation of a seed) is halted at one vital point—the division of the half-chromosomes.

These chromosomes are the tiny bodies in a cell which carry over the qualities of a species from one generation to the next. Normally, when two sex cells are united, as by the pollenation of a plant ovary, they have first a double nucleus. This divides into offspring nuclei. Thus the seed, or the new plant, begun by doubling its number of chromosomes, ends up by having only the same number as its parents. In this way the specific characteristics of a flower's color, shape, size, and fragrance remains unchanged. But colchicine, by preventing this division into offspring or half-chromosomes, gives the new individual double the usual number of chromosomes, creating a new rose or radish, as the case may be.

This experimentation, like soilless gardening, had hardly begun before the Second World War drafted the interests and energies of scientists into other fields. Indications are that no type of plant material, from forage grasses to forest trees, fails to react to the magic touch of colchicine.

Two Geneva, N. Y. scientists have declared: "We predict that vegetables, cereals, and fodder plants (in particular) may be changed during the next twenty years as much as they have been transformed in the last two hundred . . . With fruits the greatest changes will come in the genus *Prunus,* among the cherries, plums, apricots, and peaches . . . New forms may be confidently expected in the small fruits, especially currants and gooseberries and probably in raspberries and blackberries; but not in strawberries, in which, as in apples, pears, and grapes, chromosomal evolution . . . may have proceeded to its natural limits without the help of man." [2]

Colchicine is not the only means being used in experi-

ments to transform existing plants. X rays, light rays, and other physical methods of development and treatment also have been added recently to the list of miracle-makers. Through chemistry and physics, man has demonstrated that he can reach down into germ plasma and remould the raw material of creation nearer to his needs.

Something Better Rather than Something New

The nation also is rich in field stations and experimental farms, where modern plant breeding is being conducted and tests of new material being made. Each State has at least one such experiment station, Federally operated, and there are more than a few privately supported organizations. Formerly, plant hunters ransacked the far fringes of the world for new plants that would be of advantage to American farmers. Today, or at least when the war ends, that search will continue. But now it is not so much something new that is required, but something better.

For example, at the University of New Hampshire, horticulturists are seeking to develop plants which will mature before the early coming of the frosts. Already a new tomato has been perfected, which ripens at least a month before standard varieties. It can be grown further north than tomatoes have ever been grown before. It is a new item for many Northern farmers. Plants from various sources, chosen for desired qualities, were crossbred. Their progeny were selected and crossbred until the desired short-season material was produced. To Dr. A. F. Yeager, noted plant breeder, this new tomato is one of his latest triumphs.

Other New Hampshire University scientists are similarly working with melons, eggplants, chrysanthemums,

RAISING SHEEP FOR FUR
Young Persian lamb, a link in the chain between
sheep imported from Bokhara and future
fur-bearing sheep for American farms

fruits, squash, and many other common crop plants. They are seeking not to find new plants but to construct better plants. Many organizations delve into creating disease-resistant stocks. What they are doing in one place is also being accomplished elsewhere. Scientific research has already added many millions of dollars of farm wealth to the nation and it promises to add billions more.

Animal Technology

Animal technology, less spectacular perhaps than plant development, has had its triumphs; and its work promises great things when the war-torn world returns to normal. One type of this work with animals has been the founding of breeding farms from which, it seems likely, superior germ plasma may be created and distributed. This is a basic experiment which strikes out far beyond conventional methods and practices.

Shorthorn cattle, for an example, have been bred so that they can reach the weight of 900 pounds in a little more than a year. This is an increase of some fifty per cent over average normal development. Similarly, rapidly growing strains of swine and sheep have been developed —veritable meat factories.

Stock is being bred, not for size alone, but also in an effort to produce breeds which will thrive in less favorable sections where there is poorer feeding. Cattle are being crossed, for example, with such types as Guzerat and Africander, in the hope of creating a new line. These are expected to withstand the heat and drought of the South and Southwest and to be more resistant to certain vexatious insects and parasites. Research is aimed at breeding of animals more indifferent to dietary deficien-

cies, such as lack of iron in Florida and lack of phosphates in the coastal plains and in the Southwest. Related to this work is the laboratory investigation of the protein, mineral, and vitamin content of various forage plants. The behavior of these plants under various methods of storage and of treatment (with such things as molasses) is a point of scientific study.

Poultry has not escaped attention. While the average hen of the farmer's casually acquired and maintained flock may produce about eighty eggs a year, superior birds have been developed which produce rather more than 200 eggs a year—some even as many as 300 a year. Turkeys, even now the most difficult of birds to raise, have been improved in strength and developed into a smaller and somewhat bigger-breasted bird, which has a larger proportion of white meat to dark than does the standard bird. This breeding of the smaller turkey is a distinct accomplishment in meeting a specific consumer demand.

Just as plant diseases and pests are being studied, so livestock ills are being investigated, particularly in the South, where warmth and dampness seem to make liver and kidney parasites more active. Gratifying success has already attended some of these studies. The cattle tick, for example, is headed towards extermination. Cattle tuberculosis has been cut to less than half of one per cent. Bang's disease, an infectious abortion trouble, is still very serious but its control is being undertaken. Hookworm, anthrax, and similar ills are responding to strict quarantine measures.

Insects exact a toll set by the Department of Agriculture at something near two billion dollars a year from the farmer's pocket. Formerly, farmers fought bugs by

handpicking them, as from potatoes. Sometimes they used handpumps to squirt sprays. Such hand labor is nearly ended. Insect fighting, thanks to the war, has developed amazingly. With power sprayers, power dusters, new and better insecticides, insect fighting is becoming a specialized but very effective technique.

Then there is the matter of fertilizing. Modern farm soils are very differently fed than was the case even a generation ago. By means of a simple analysis, ordinarily performed free of charge by Governmental agencies, a farmer can learn not merely what chemical salts his soil needs to be properly productive, but precisely how much of each salt his soil needs.

Chemists use the pH value, a shorthand symbol for hydrogen-ion analysis, and so write out a prescription for an ailing soil, just as a doctor writes out a remedy for a sick man. Today, with the virgin resources of our soil depleted through overcropping, erosion, and other abuses, the chemist is a vital element in the farm picture.

The chemist is concerned with the production of food that is properly nutritious. The white sand of certain Florida coastal sections can grow almost anything well enough for ornamental horticulture; but when food is produced, it is another matter. A potato may look perfect, but if the soil in which it was grown lacked sufficient minerals, then that potato is not as good a food for human use as a potato grown in a soil that has all the minerals.

The problem of fertilizing is a vast one. The physical bulk of fertilizers needed is amazing, and the industry is constantly expanding. Sources of supply are thus of tremendous importance. Scientists had a recent success in developing an electrical process of extracting nitrogen

from the air so cheaply that it can be sold in bags as fertilizer for farm fields. This is as great an achievement as
the winning of a critical battle. It *is* a battle—waged with
test tubes instead of with rifles. It is the kind of battle on
which the destiny of every person in the world depends,
for we all must eat.

The Weather

There is still another scientific contribution being made
to the farmer and to everyone else. This is the weather
service.

Weather forecasting was an art a few years ago. Today
it is an abstruse science which is becoming more mathematical by the hour. Balloon-carried robot-radio stations
soar into the stratosphere and send back reports on the
weather miles overhead. From every corner of the world,
hour by hour, day after day, reports of the weather come
in. Forecasters sitting in Washington know what is hap-
pening at the Poles as well as in New York City. The forecasts they make for today and tomorrow are far more accurate than was thought possible only yesterday.

Meanwhile, the meteorologists, working in scientific
co-operation that transcends political boundaries, are developing new theories of the weather. Forecasting, to
name the part of most interest to every farmer, is no
longer just a matter of a few hours ahead. Forecasts are
being made for weeks, for months, for seasons, and for
complete cycles.

However, these long-range forecasts have not yet
proved themselves completely reliable, and hence are not
yet made known to the public. Indications are that it will
not be long before they can be safely published. Then

farmers will have real help in planning their planting. If it is known a year ahead that a drought is coming, farmers in the Dust Bowl may be able to prevent dust storms. Elsewhere, farmers knowing that the summer will be wet or dry, cool or hot, as the case may be, can schedule their work to make the most of the weather.

Chemurgy

This outline of science enlisted in the service of the farmer could be continued for page after page—soil erosion, Dust Bowl control, irrigation, marketing, co-operatives. In these and many other problems, chemists, physicists, biologists, economists, and other specialists are busy. As a result of this mobilization of intelligence, it may be that in the day to come the farmer will no longer be a helpless victim of circumstance. Uncertainty has plagued the growing of crops and the raising of cattle ever since farming began. Tomorrow may see the end of the curse.

This hope gains substance, too, because lately a new element has appeared in the American farmer's life. This is the industrial utilization of farm products directly as raw materials for fabricating buildings, ships, and hundreds of other things. Of course, the farmer has always fed raw materials to industry—wool, cotton, wood, and hides, for example; and indirectly, the farmer has fed industry its bread and its butter. But this chemurgy is something new; for now industry will tell the farmer what he can grow; what industry needs from the farm as the basic substances out of which it will fabricate articles for the market.

The name of chemurgy has been given to this development because the chemist is the person most concerned.

In effect, if chemurgy increases (as present indications promise) the chemist may take command of agriculture.

There are various and confused political, social, and economic considerations arrayed in rather discouraging opposition; but it seems likely that after the war the farmer will have the chemist not only as his ally but as his captain. It will be the chemist who will develop agriculture, formerly largely only a means of food production, so that it will be also a partner in the factory. The fields and the meadows will not only feed us, they will grow the raw materials for houses and planes just as they now grow clothes and dinners.

This will mean not merely increased markets for farm products; but by removing many acres from the inefficient production of food, will make an end of overproduction. Farm prices will be stabilized at reasonable levels, because food will be grown mostly on suitable land and in adequate amounts. Surplus farm acreage and submarginal land can be put to work by the chemist.

Just what miracles the chemist will work tomorrow may not yet be published. That many new substances have been established is unquestioned; but in the warring forties little is known about them. However, what chemurgy had already accomplished before Pearl Harbor can be used to indicate what it will accomplish.

In general, chemistry plans to use three major farm products.

First, there is cellulose, the familiar material out of which trees and grasses are composed. A wooden house is a house of cellulose. Paper is cellulose. So are cotton cloth and linen. Because of inefficient methods in lumbering and manufacturing, we have wasted more cellu-

MODERN CHEMURGY
Spraying tomatoes with hormone solution
to set fruit

lose than we have consumed. Every weed that grows, every cornstalk, every grain of dust in the sawdust pile, every chip of wood, and every lopped bough in the forest is wasted cellulose.

Chemists have known for years that this cellulose can be made into food, starch, sugar, and alcohol; but there was no need of doing so, because we had enough of those products from other sources. Then, before Pearl Harbor, chemists made their first great advance in the use of cellulose as a raw material. This was the creation of fibers from wood—rayon, for example. Women began to wear dresses and stockings made of glorified wood. The silkworm was dethroned; and in far-off Japan, famine faced thousands of silk workers.

Rayon has been only a beginning. It has competitors in other fibers, such as nylon—those made from milk, coal, and other sources. There is no question but that fibers and plastics made from cellulose have a tremendously important future.

Plastics (chemically made) and wood itself, sliced into thin slabs and compounded with various bonding plastics, may be the magic materials of the next decade. As hard as steel, as light as aluminum, weatherproof, rustproof, and termite-proof, cellulose seems to be the ideal material for building—to mention but one use. The farmer, under the command of the chemist, can grow houses, ships, furniture, and a thousand other products right in the cornfield and the wood lot, in the form of cellulose.

The second major field into which farm products will be channeled by chemurgy will be that of oil. The farmer, even now, can transform his acres into oil wells, if he chooses, and make money by so doing without selling any

stock to his neighbors. The loss of imported vegetable oils and fats from the Far East by reason of Japanese conquest merely pointed the need of America for vast amounts of vegetable oils. Cottonseed oil and linseed oil, always staples, have boomed in importance; and with them the other vegetable oils came into the limelight. Soybeans are not only a source of food and of plastics but also a source of valuable oil. So are more than a dozen other plants and trees (such as tung) which have been imported into this country and are being promoted as sources of oil. These the farmer can grow profitably, if soil and climate are suitable.

The increasing market comes not only from medicinal and lubricating uses, as with the familiar castor bean. For one thing, oils are being used in increasingly large amounts in the production of varnishes, paints, and lacquers. These finishes are of value in proportion to the character of the film which they develop over the surfaces they cover and protect.

This process is largely a matter of "oxidation." Petroleum oils do not oxidize properly, but vegetable oils do; and, what is most important, many oxidize quickly. Thus the modern quick-drying finishes have been developed. Today, an automobile can be painted in an hour. Yesterday, weeks were required, because the drying time needed between each two coats was days instead of minutes.

The farmer has still another and perhaps the most important chemurgical use for his acres. This is the growing of starches and sugars for their transformation into alcohol by the chemical industry.

The subject of alcohol production is a complex one, for modern research has indicated that "grain alcohol," such

as was formerly produced from grains and was the only alcohol suitable for beverage purposes, can now be produced also from wood. Formerly wood produced only "wood" alcohol, which was poisonous as a beverage but useful in industry for certain purposes. And these two alcohols are but the best-known of many alcohols. Research indicates that the chemical industry can also produce from farm crops such vital materials as acetic acid, acetone, aldehydes (furfural), phenols, and a multitude of other things.

When the story of the Second World War is written, the work of the American chemists will be one of the most astonishing and most triumphant epics of the entire pattern. It is a long cry from a bushel of corn in an Iowa corncrib to a rubber tire rolling along on an American jeep in Germany—but that is a sample of what chemurgy is accomplishing at the request of war.

Out of Uniform

Such things as "woolen cloth" from milk, paints that are really only a step away from the soybean, furniture that was cornstalks only a few weeks before—these modern miracles are but a few of the tricks the chemist of the future has in mind.

There are wonderful things ahead. Only five hundred years ago the farmer was a serf or a slave on the estate of some European noble. Three hundred years ago he began to escape from his narrow circumstances in the Old World to the opportunities of "free land" in America. Through the centuries, while there have been mistakes and abuses, the farmer has prospered here. He is no slave, no serf. In many ways, he is, of all men, the most free.

Now, after two great wars, the farmer stands ready to take an important place in the days ahead. This time, for once in the history of the world, he has a voice along with the merchant, the banker, and the industrialist. The farmer can take part in shaping what is to be—and in this work he has the help of the scientists, particularly the chemist.

Farming is a way of life. It will always be that, for it has values beyond money, satisfactions greater than things which can be bought and sold. Tomorrow, farming will be a wider, a deeper, and altogether a better way of life than it ever has been before. It will take time and study; co-operation and experiment; but the groundwork has already been laid.

[1] Ellis, Carleton and Swaney, Millar W. *Soilless Growth of Plants*. New York. 1938
[2] Nebel, R. B. and Ruttle, M. L. *Use of Chemicals in Plant Breeding. Farm Research*. N. Y. State Agricultural Experiment Station. Geneva, N. Y. July 1, 1938

CONCLUSION

JUST what will be the experience of farmers in the years ahead? The question is of world-wide significance and has already produced a flood of printed material, mostly statistics and opinion. Here in America there are apparently two main factors dominant in the solution which the future will reveal.

The first one is simply that our geographical means of expansion is ended. There is no more frontier. We can no longer escape from the consequences of our past wasteful economic follies by tapping fresh sources of natural wealth. We must make the most of what we have.

"We must give up our life of adolescence and become a mature and stable culture. Our extensive and quantitative frontiers are gone; those of the future must be intensive and qualitative." [1]

The second factor is, in simplest terms, this: The United States is now definitely established with an urban rather than a rural culture. The truth is that of the 130,000,000 Americans, there were in 1944 about 27,000,000 persons tabulated by the Government as "total farm population." [2]

One of the greatest modern American historians declares: "America is a land of science, machinery, mass production, imperial finance, and great cities. And our urban economy is corporate, not competitive." [3]

323

What will these two influences mean for the farmer tomorrow, especially for the thousands who go farmward marching as this war ends?

The first influence, the end of the frontier, with no more free land for anyone, means that the farmer must become much more highly skilled than has been the case before. He must not abuse his land, because there is no more virgin soil waiting for exploitation.

Two developments could result from this necessity of the proper use of land—and neither of them is traditionally desirable to the American farmer.

The farmer more and more must lean on science. He must not only know more, must not only be really educated in his own technologies, but he must employ machines that will make his efforts more efficient and multiply his time and energy. Hence, more and more capital will be required. This might mean that the day of the independent individual farmer would soon end. In his place might appear huge corporate structures—farms of thousands of acres managed by boards of directors and employing salaried experts and executives. There might also be a co-operative development, instead of, or together with, the formal corporation.

On these superfarms, whether co-operative or corporative, mechanization would be almost complete. Fewer and fewer hands would be employed. Fewer farmers, by far, would be needed. Perhaps only one man in ten would need to be a farmer.

As a further result of this giganticism, the superfarms would appropriate the best farm lands in the nation. For capital must make profits; to make profits, production must exceed costs; and this is possible only by the utiliza-

tion of the best of materials—in this case, land. Hence large areas of the poorer lands now under cultivation of a sort, would revert either to grazing areas or else to forestry—which in themselves would probably become the province of large organizations efficiently managed.

All this would mean an elevation of rural standards of living to the point where they would approximate urban conditions. Every farm community would be large enough to have good schools, good hospitals, electric power, and all the rest. But it is a threat to the independent farmer.

If this highly scientific agriculture, with consequent urbanization and consequent release of many millions of Americans from farming, does not come about, then another development might take place.

This is the establishment of a permanent peasantry. All the older nations of the world, such as China and Russia, have their economy based more or less upon a peasant farmer. Only our youth as a nation may have saved us from it—so far. Farmers would, if this happens, fail more and more to share in the distribution of wealth. The larger staple crops would probably fall into corporate hands. Large areas would be taken over by industrial organizations. Cotton mills would become proprietors of cotton plantations operated by employees. Cigarette factories would own the tobacco lands. Flour mills would own the wheatlands, and so on. The farmer would be simply a governed wage earner, just like a mechanic on a production line in an automobile factory.

All the farmers left outside this sphere might retain their independence. The Government would not greatly care, for such farmers would be numerically unimportant. Gradually they would lack the capital to own ma-

chines or the ability to market their products efficiently. Slowly, these little farmers, though they might continue to own their lands, would sink back toward the subsistence level. Farming might swing back full cycle to colonial conditions—so far as it would be possible in modern times. Such a development, however, would be altogether un-American, for it would mean the end of our traditional ambition for improvement and progress. But it could happen.

However, it is very unlikely to happen, for there is the other major factor in the farm picture—the development of urbanity.

Traditionally, the condition of urbanity means to be polished, or cultivated. In American terms, it means to be educated. And in education the American farmer, whether large farm corporations arise or not, has his great hope of the future in education.

The American has always had a somewhat naive faith in general education as a panacea for all ills. Nearly everyone accepts the belief that the better a farmer is educated, the better a farmer he will be.

However, what is meant here by "education" goes further. It would make possible an agriculture in which experts, both in the sciences and in the humanities, would maintain the nation safely above the level of old-time peasantry. It would combat those destructive forces which might entail a return to barbarism.

Education in this sense could develop a new frontier for American farmers. Just as we have recently astonished the world by our industrial triumph of mass production of the tools of destruction, so can trained and directed intelligence create a new farming era of superlative quality.

If the history of American agriculture means anything, it gives hope that this will be the future for our farms and farmers. Unless all the world collapses, and even if much of it slips back for a while into misery as the aftermath of the Second World War, the future for the American farmer, with science, seems bright.

There is much to be done. A throng of problems await scientific solution. But in the past three hundred years the American mind has triumphed over many difficulties; and American ingenuity should be no less successful in the days to come.

In the preceding pages the history of American agriculture has been related. In large part it is the story of men marching across the nation, led by the shining star of freedom. "Free land!" has been the epitome of the American farmer. The land has now been entirely taken up, but the farmer still has that which his free land gave him—freedom from serfdom.

And it is in freedom that our farmers—men, women and children—continue toward the new frontier of urbane, or controlled, organized, *educated* farming.

[1] Speech, Carl C. Taylor, Director of Rural Resettlement, Resettlement Administration. Columbus, Ohio. Sept. 19, 1935

[2] Testimony, Senate Special Committee on Postwar Economic Policy. May 11, 1944

[3] Beard, Charles A. *Culture and Agriculture.* Saturday Review of Literature. October 20, 1928

APPENDIX

AN AGRICULTURAL CHRONOLOGY

Compiled (1776-1939) by Arthur P. Chew, United States Department of Agriculture, Washington, D. C.

1776—John Adams introduces resolutions in Continental Congress to encourage agriculture.

1796—George Washington (last annual message) makes an appeal for a national board of agriculture.

1820—House of Representatives appoints agricultural committee.

1825—Senate appoints agricultural committee.

1839—Congress appropriates $1,000 to collect and distribute seeds, conduct agricultural investigations, collect agricultural statistics. Patent Office assumes the work.

1862—Organic Act (May 15, R. S. sec. 520) establishes the Dept. of Agri. for acquiring and diffusing information relating to agriculture.

1862—First Homestead Act (May 20, Chap. 75, 12 Stat. 392).

1862—First Morrill Act (July 2) donates land for colleges of agricultural and mechanic arts.

1884—Act of May 29 (23 Stat. 31) to prevent the spread of contagious diseases among cattle; establishes the Bureau of Animal Industry.

1887—Agricultural Experiment Stations Act (Mar. 2, 24 Stat. 440) authorizes the establishment, under the direction of the land-grant colleges for which provision was made by the act of July 2, 1862 (12 Stat. 503), of experiment stations to conduct experiments relating to agricultural subjects.

1889—Act of February 9 (25 Stat. 659) makes the Dept. of Agri. an executive department.

1890—Second Morrill Act (Aug. 30) provides for the further endowment of land-grant colleges.

1890—The Weather Service Act (Oct. 1, 26 Stat. 653) establishes the Weather Bureau.

1891—National-forest system begins. Congress authorizes President to set aside forest reserves from the public domain.

1905—Act of February 1 (33 Stat. 628) places under the jurisdiction of the Sec. of Agri. the protection of national forests.

1905—Animal Quarantine Act (Mar. 3, 43 Stat. 1264) prevents spread of diseases of livestock by regulating their interstate movement from areas affected with contagious diseases.

1905—Act of March 3 (33 Stat. 1269) prohibits interstate transportation of enumerated insect pests.

1906—Food and Drugs Act (June 30, 34 Stat. 768) prohibits shipment in interstate commerce of articles of food and drug that are adulterated or misbranded.

1907—Meat Inspection Act (Mar. 4, 34 Stat. 1260) authorizes inspection of slaughtering or packing establishments of meats moving in interstate or foreign commerce and the destruction of condemned meats.

1908—Inspection of Dairy Products for Export Act (May 23, 35 Stat. 254) provides for inspection and certification as to purity and quality of dairy products intended for export; also marketing, stamping, and labeling of such products.

1910—Insecticides Act (Apr. 26, 36 Stat. 331) prohibits transportation or selling in interstate commerce of adulterated or misbranded insecticides and fungicides.

1911—Weeks Act (Mar. 1, 36 Stat. 961) authorizes States to enter into compacts for the conservation of forests and water supplies, and sets up National Forest Reservation Commission to pass upon recommendations of the Secretary for purchase of lands necessary to the regulation of the flow of navigable streams.

1912—Plant Quarantine Act (Aug. 20, 37 Stat. 315) regulates importation and interstate movement of plants, plant products, and other commodities to prevent introduction into and the spread within the United States of injurious plant diseases and pests.

1912—Federal Seed Act (Aug. 24, 37 Stat. 506), as amended, prohibits importation of seeds which are adulterated or unfit for planting purposes.

1914—Agricultural Extension Act of May 8 (38 Stat. 372), authorizes cooperative work with land-grant colleges in giving instruction in agriculture and home economics to persons not attending said colleges.

1916—Grain Standards Act (Aug. 11, 39 Stat. 482) provides for uniformity in grading of grain by authorizing the Sec. of Agri. to establish standards of quality and condition of grain.

1916—United States Cotton Futures Act (Aug. 11, 39 Stat. 476) lays a tax of 2 cents a pound on cotton involved in contracts of sale of cotton for future delivery upon exchange unless certain types of contracts are used.

1916—Warehouse Act (Aug. 11, 39 Stat. 486) provides for licensing by Sec.

of Agri. of warehouses in which agricultural commodities are stored for shipment in interstate commerce.

1921—Packers and Stockyards Act (Aug. 15, 42 Stat. 159) regulates business practices of packers in interstate commerce, of stockyard owners or operators, and of commission merchants and others; prohibits unfair, unjustly discriminatory, and deceptive practices and devices.

1922—Commodity Exchange Act, known as the Grain Futures Act (42 Stat. 998), until amended June 15, 1936, regulates exchanges, commission merchants, and brokers dealing in future contracts covering wheat, cotton, rice, corn, oats, barley, rye, flax, seed grain, sorghums, mill feeds, butter, eggs, and potatoes. Provides for elimination of certain practices such as manipulation of the market, corners and squeezes, and making of false reports. Commission merchants and floor brokers required to register with the Sec. of Agri.

1923—Naval Stores Act (Mar. 3, 42 Stat. 1435) provides for promulgation by the Sec. of Agri. of official standards for resin and turpentine; requires that all resin and turpentine shipped in interstate commerce shall be sold under or by reference to such standards.

1923—Cotton Standards Act (Mar. 4, 42 Stat. 1517) provides for establishment of standards of quality of cotton; forbids use of other than official standards in transactions in interstate commerce and in the publication of prices or quotations determined in or in connection with such transactions; authorizes an inspection service.

1927—Import Milk Act (Feb. 15, 44 Stat. 1101) to prevent importation of milk and cream that do not comply with health requirements specifically designated therein.

1927—Produce Agency Act (Mar. 3, 44 Stat. 1355) makes it a criminal offense for any person receiving fruits, vegetables, melons, dairy or poultry products, or perishable farm products in interstate commerce for or on behalf of another to fail truly and correctly to account therefor, or to make false reports or statements relating to handling or disposition of same.

1927—Act of March 3 (44 Stat. 1372), as amended to 1937, authorizes Sec. of Agri. to collect and publish cotton statistics; to require certain persons to furnish information upon which to base statistics; to make available to requesting producers classification of cotton produced by them; and to make public market information on cotton, issue crop and acreage reports.

1930—Foreign Agricultural Service Act (June 5, 46 Stat. 497) authorizes establishment of foreign agricultural service for acquiring information regarding quality, competition, and demand for agricultural products, and the production, marketing, and distribution of such products in foreign countries.

1930—Perishable Agricultural Commodities Act (June 10, 46 Stat. 531), as amended, requires licensing of commission merchants, dealers, and brokers handling fresh fruits and vegetables in interstate commerce; enumerates certain kinds of unfair conduct which it declares unlawful.

1933—Agricultural Adjustment Act (May 12, 48 Stat. 31), several times amended, to establish and maintain such balance between the production and consumption of agricultural commodities and such marketing conditions as would reestablish prices to farmers at a level that would give agricultural commodities a purchasing power with respect to articles that farmers buy equivalent to the purchasing power of agricultural commodities in the base period (August 1909-July 1914; except August 1919-July 1929 for tobacco and potatoes).

1934—Sugar Act (Jones-Costigan Act) (May 9, 48 Stat. 670), amendment to the Agricultural Adjustment Act and later amended, provides for making benefit payments to producers of sugar, a tax on the processing of sugar, and quota allotments to restrict the amount of sugar imported as well as the amount moving in interstate commerce.

1935—Soil Erosion Act (Apr. 27, 49 Stat. 163) establishes Soil Conservation Service to prevent soil erosion and preserve natural resources, control floods, maintain navigability of rivers and harbors; to conduct investigations and research; carry out preventive measures either on Federal lands or by co-operative agreements with agencies and persons controlling other lands; and contribute services, equipment, money, or materials.

1935—Act of June 29 (49 Stat. 436) authorized the Sec. of Agri. to conduct research into basic laws and principles of agriculture; provides for development of extension work.

1935—Section 32 of the act to amend the Agricultural Adjustment Act, and for other purposes (approved Aug. 24, 49 Stat. 750), authorizes Sec. of Agri. to make payments for encouraging exportation and domestic consumption of agricultural commodities and products thereof; and, in order to reestablish farmers' purchasing power, to make payments in connection with the normal production of any agricultural commodity for domestic consumption.

1936—Soil Conservation and Domestic Allotment Act (Feb. 29, 49 Stat. 1148) stresses as its objective, in addition to those present in the Soil Erosion Act, the preservation and improvement of soil fertility and promotion of the economic use and conservation of lands, by the encouragement of soil-conserving and soil-rebuilding practices rather than the growing of soil-depleting commercial crops. By the terms and the act, appropriations may be made available to the States upon their passing an approved State plan which will carry out the objectives of the act. Pending the enactment of State legislation, the statute permits payments to individual agricultural producers.

1936—Flood Control Act of June 22 (49 Stat. 1570) authorizes the Sec. of Agri. to conduct investigations of watersheds and measures for run-off and water-flow retardation. The act of August 28, 1937 (50 Stat. 876), and the Flood Control Act of 1938, approved June 28, 1938 (52 Stat. 1215), augment the 1936 Act by authorizing the Sec. of Agri. to examine and survey for water-flow retardation and soil-erosion prevention purposes the watersheds of all waterways which the Sec. of War is authorized to survey for flood-control purposes; and to undertake active measures for water-flow retardation in accordance with plans approved by the Secretary of Agriculture.

1936—Act of April 26 (49 Stat. 1239) establishes Congressional consent for tobacco-producing States to enter into "essentially uniform" compacts controlling production of or commerce in tobacco for the purpose of enabling growers to receive fair prices; empowers the Sec. of Agri. to advance funds to States, subject to repayment, to defray administrative expenses arising out of compacts, to make loans to Georgia Tobacco Belt producers, and to render official advice and make Department records, information, and facilities available to compacting parties.

1937—Co-operative Farm Forestry Act (May 18, 50 Stat. 188), to aid agriculture, increase farm-forest income, conserve water resources, and increase employment by co-operation between Sec. of Agri. and colleges, forest agencies and individual farmers in planting trees and shrubs, in establishing and managing farm-forests and in developing nursery sites for this purpose.

1937—Agricultural Marketing Agreement Act of 1937 (June 3, 50 Stat. 246) authorizes the Sec. of Agri. to enter into marketing agreements and, in the case of certain specified commodities, to issue orders regulating the handling of agricultural commodities by fixing grade, size, or quantity of such commodities that may be shipped and, in the case of milk, by fixing minimum prices to be paid producers.

1937—Bankhead-Jones Farm Tenant Act (July 22, 50 Stat. 522) authorizes (1) loans to farm tenants and other eligible individuals to enable them to acquire farms; (2) rehabilitation loans to eligible individuals for operating and subsistence needs; and (3) a program of land conservation and land utilization, including retirement of submarginal lands.

1937—Act of August 28 (50 Stat. 869) recognizes wastage and incomplete utilization of water resources on farm, grazing and forest lands, resulting from inadequate water storage facilities; authorizes the Sec. of Agri. to formulate and keep current a program of projects for construction and maintenance of ponds, reservoirs, wells, check-dams, etc.; to sell, lease, or allow free use of such facilities.

1937—The Sugar Act of 1937 (September 1, 50 Stat. 503) provides for regulation of sugar-marketing in interstate and foreign commerce by imposition of quotas on the continental United States, the offshore possessions and foreign countries; protects consumers against excessive prices by authorizing the Sec. of Agri. to adjust his estimate of consumption requirements, which forms the basis of the quotas, so that under ordinary circumstances the total supply of sugar made available will not be less than that necessary to give consumers a per capita consumption equal to the average of the 2-year period 1935-1936; and, in order to adjust marketings of sugar cane and sugar beets in continental United States, Hawaii, and Puerto Rico to sugar marketings permitted under quota provisions, provides for conditional payments to producers in those areas.

1938—Agricultural Adjustment Act of 1938 (February 16, 52 Stat. 31), empowers Sec. of Agri. to conserve nation's soil resources and promote their efficient use as part of a permanent farm policy; to assist in marketing of farm products for domestic consumption and export by establishing acreage allotments for which payment may be made to co-operating farmers; to regulate interstate commerce in cotton, wheat, corn, tobacco and rice, so as to minimize violent fluctuations in supplies, marketing and prices o˙ farm commodities, protect consumers by maintaining adequate reserves of food and feed, and assure farmers a fair share of national income.

1938—Federal Crop Insurance Act (February 16, 52 Stat. 72) creates, as an agency of Dept. of Agri., in order to promote national welfare by alleviating the economic distress caused by wheat crop failures, through the maintenance of purchasing power of farmers, and by stabilizing supplies of wheat, the Federal Crop Insurance Corporation; with a board of three directors appointed by the Sec. of Agri. and empowered to conduct researches, surveys, and investigations on crop insurance for wheat and other agricultural commodities; and, commencing with the wheat crop of 1939, to insure producers against loss of yields; to purchase, handle, store, insure, provide storage facilities for, and sell

wheat; and pay any expenses incident thereto in connection with crop insurance.

1938—Insect Control Act (May 9, 52 Stat. 344) empowers Sec. of Agri. to co-operate with States, organizations, or individuals in applying methods of control to incipient or emergency outbreaks of insect pests or plant diseases, and authorizes annual appropriations for such purposes.

1938—Federal Food, Drug, and Cosmetic Act (June 25, 52 Stat. 1040), prohibits the movement in interstate commerce of articles of food, drugs, devices, and cosmetics that are adulterated or misbranded; of any new drug that the Secretary finds to be unsafe under conditions prescribed, recommended, or suggested in its labeling; and of any article of food that may be contaminated under certain conditions if the Secretary has not issued a permit as to the same. The act authorizes the seizure of such articles and provides for injunction against and prosecution of their shipper.

1939—Federal Seed Act (August 9, 7 USC 1551-1610) to regulate foreign and interstate commerce in specified agricultural seeds and to prevent unfair practices.

1939—Reorganization plans (various dates) place in the Dept. of Agri. the Bureau of Public Roads, the Farm Credit Administration, the Federal Farm Mortgage Corporation, the Commodity Credit Corporation, and the Rural Electrification Administration.

1940—Reorganization plans (April 2 and 11) created the Surplus Marketing Administration in the Dept. of Agri. by combining the Division of Marketing and Marketing Agreements of the Agricultural Adjustment Administration and the Federal Surplus Commodities Corporation, and transferred the Weather Bureau to the Department of Commerce.

1941—Sec. of Agri. authorized to support a price for the producers of any non-basic agricultural commodity at 85 per cent of the parity or comparable price. (July 1, 15 USC 713—by Act of Oct. 2, rate was increased from 85 to 90 per cent.)

1941—Lend Lease Act (March 11, 22 USC 411-19) providing for lease, loan, etc. of war materials, including agricultural commodities or articles in the interests of the defense of the United States.

1942—Rubber Act (March 5, 7 USC 171) authorizing the Sec. of Agri. to administer a program for the developing of guayule and other rubber-bearing plants.

1942—An act (Oct. 2, 56 Stat. 765) setting forth the formula for determining the price below which no maximum price shall be established for any

agricultural commodity; and authorizing and directing the Commodity Credit Corporation to make loans upon cotton, corn, wheat, rice, tobacco, and peanuts at specified rates. Pursuant to this act, Executive Order 9250 was issued, authorizing the Sec. of Agri. and the Price Administrator jointly to establish or maintain or adjust prices of agricultural commodities.

1943—(Executive Order 9328, April 10) further directing the Administrators of Food Production and Distribution and the Price Administrator to stabilize prices of agricultural commodities.

1943—An act (April 29, 57 Stat. 70) authorizing the War Food Administration to assist in providing an adequate supply of workers for production and harvesting of essential agricultural commodities.

1941-1945—The Farmer At War (A Summary of Federal Agricultural Regulation and Support).

1941—After Pearl Harbor the American Farmer was called upon by the President to play a vital part in the winning of the War. Though crippled by the loss of manpower, by lack of tools and other materials and machinery, the farms of the nation were made to produce more food than had been dreamed possible. The patriotic farmers fed not only America but much of the rest of the world. A complete, detailed chronological history of this period has been prepared by the U. S. Dept. of Agriculture, Washington, D. C.: *Abridged Chronology of Agriculture's Part in the War*, No. 3, Revised Edition, Oct. 2, 1944.

BIBLIOGRAPHY

Andrews, Charles M. *Colonial Folkways*. New Haven. 1919

Baker, Oliver E. *Agricultural Regions of North America. Economic Geography*. October, 1926; April, 1933

Baker, O. E., Ralph Borsodi and M. L. Wilson, *Agriculture in Modern Life*. New York. 1939

Beard, Charles Austin and Mary Ritter Beard, *The Rise of American Civilization*. 2 v. New York. 1927

Beard, Charles Austin and Mary Ritter Beard. *Basic History of the U. S.* New York. 1944

Bidwell, Percy Welles and John I. Falconer. *History of Agriculture in the Northern United States*. Carnegie Institution of Washington. Washington. 1925

Black, J. D. *Agricultural Reforms in the United States*. New York. 1929

Bogart, Ernest Ludlow. *Economic History of American Agriculture*. New York. 1923

Bogart, Ernest Ludlow. *Economic History of the American People*. New York. 1935

Bolles, Albert Sidney. *Industrial History of the United States*. Norwich, Conn. 1878

Borsodi, Ralph. *Prosperity and Security*. New York. 1937

Brewer, William H. *History of American Agriculture*. In V. 3, 10th Census. United States Bureau of the Census. Washington. 1880

Bruce, Philip A. *Economic History of Virginia*. New York. 1896

Buck, S. J. *The Granger Movement*. Cambridge. 1913

Buck, S. J. *The Agrarian Crusade*. New Haven. 1921

Browne, Daniel J. *Encouragement of Agriculture in the United States*. Annual Report, United States Commissioner of Patents. Washington. 1857

Callender, Guy Stevens, Ed. *Selections from the Economic History of the United States, 1765-1860*. Boston. 1909

Carman, H. J. et al. *Historic Currents in Changing America*. Philadelphia. 1938

Capper, Arthur. *A Hundred Years of Agriculture*. In *A Century of Progress*, edited by Frederic W. Wile. Garden City. 1928

Carrier, Lyman. *The Beginnings of Agriculture in America*. New York. 1923

Carver, Thomas Nixon. *Principles of Rural Economics*. Boston. 1932

Carver, T. N. *Agriculture in the United States, Encyclopedia Americana*, New York. 1932

Carver, T. N. *Historical Sketch of American Agriculture*. In *Cyclopedia of American Agriculture*. L. H. Bailey, Ed. New York. 1912

Channing, Edward. *History of the United States*. 5 V. New York. 1905-1921

Chew, Arthur P. *The Response of Government to Agriculture*. United States Department of Agriculture. Washington. 1937

Clark, Victor S. *History of Manufactures in the United States, 1607-1860*. Carnegie Institution of Washington. Washington. 1916

The Country Gentleman. Philadelphia. Files of this magazine are invaluable.

DeKruif, Paul. *Hunger Fighters*. New York. 1938

Edwards, Everett E. *Jefferson and Agriculture*. Washington.

Faulkner, Harold Underwood. *American Economic History*. New Ed. New York. 1938

Flint, Charles Louis. *A Hundred Years' Progress of American Agriculture*. In annual report, Massachusetts Board of Agriculture. Boston. 1873

Fiskc, John. *The Beginnings of New England*. Boston. 1899

Fiske, John. *Old Virginia and Her Neighbors*. Boston. 1897

Fream, William and Roland Truslove. *Agriculture in the United States*. 11th Ed. of *Encyclopedia Britannica*. Cambridge. 1910

Fritts, Frank and Ralph Swinn. *Fifth Avenue to Farm*. New York. 1939

Gabriel, Ralph H. *Toilers of Land and Sea*. In *Pageant of America*. New Haven. 1926

Gephart, William P. *Transportation and Industrial Development in the Middle West*. In *Columbia University Studies in History, Economics, etc.* New York. 1910

Gras, Norman Scott Brien. *History of Agriculture in Europe and America*. New York. 1925

Gray, Lewis Cecil and Esther Katherine Thompson. *History of Agriculture in the Southern United States to 1860*. Carnegie Institution of Washington. Washington. 1933

Great Plains Committee. *The Future of the Great Plains*. Official Report. Washington. 1936

Gregory, Clifford V. *Farming Through the Ages*. Prairie Review. Chicago. 1928-1929

Green, John Richard. *Short History of the English People*. New York. 1898

Hale, William J. *Farmward March*. New York. 1939

Hall, J. Alfred and T. J. Mosley. *Products of American Forests*. United States Forest Service. Washington. 1939

Hart, Albert Bushnell, Ed. *The American Nation: A History*. 27 v. New York. 1904-1917

Hawthorne, Nathaniel. *American Note Books*. 11th Ed. Boston. 1887

Hedrick, Ulysses P. *History of Agriculture in New York*. Albany. 1933

Hibbard, Benjamin H. *History of Public Land Policies*. New York. 1924

Hicks, J. D. *The Populist Revolt*. New York. 1931

Higginson, Francis. *Journal and New England's Plantation* in Young's *Chronicles of Massachusetts*. Boston. 1846

Holmes, G. K. *Progress of Agriculture in the United States*. United States Department of Agriculture. Washington. 1899

James, G. W. *Reclaiming the West*. New York. 1917

Johnson, Allen, Ed. *The Chronicles of America*. 50 v. New Haven. 1919-1921

Johnson, Emory Richards and others. *History of Domestic and Foreign Commerce of the United States*. Carnegie Institution of Washington. Washington. 1915

Josselyn, John. *Account of Two Voyages*, etc. *Collections*. Massachusetts Historical Society. Boston. Various dates.

Kaempffert, Waldemar, Ed. *Popular History of American Invention*. New York. 1924

Kile, O. M. *The Farm Bureau Movement*. New York. 1921

LaFollette, Robert Marion. Ed. *The Making of America*. 5 v. Philadelphia. 1905

Lippincott, Isaac. *Economic Development of America*. 3d ed. New York. 1933

Lively, C. E. and Conrad Taeuber. *Rural Migration in the United States*. Works Progress Administration. Washington. 1939

Lodge, Henry Cabot. *Short History of the English Colonies*. New York. 1881

Lord, Russell. *To Hold This Soil*. United States Soil Conservation Service, Washington. 1938

Lowden, Frank O. *Agriculture*. In *A Century of Progress*, Edited by Charles A. Beard. New York. 1933

Mangelsdorf, P. C. and R. G. Reeves. *The Origin of Indian Corn and Its Relatives*. College Station, Texas. 1939

Massachusetts Horticultural Society. Yearbooks and various publications. Boston. 1829

Mathews, Lois Kimball. *The Expansion of New England*. Boston. 1909

McCormick, Cyrus. *The Century of the Reaper*. Boston. 1931

McCrory, S. H. et al. *Technological Trends in Relation to Agriculture*. National Resources Committee. Washington. 1937

Miller, Merritt Finley. *The Evolution of Reaping Machines*. United States Department of Agriculture. Washington. 1902

National Canners Association. *The Story of the Tin Can*. Washington. 1936

National Canners Association. *The Canning Industry*. Washington. 1939

National Canners Association. *The History of Canning.* Washington. 1939

President's Committee on Farm Tenancy. *Farm Tenancy.* Washington. 1937

Paxson, F. L. *History of the American Frontier.* New York. 1929

Perry, Josephine and Celeste Slauson. *Forestry and Lumbering.* New York. 1939

Phillips, Ulrich. *Documentary History of American Industrial Society.* Cleveland. 1910

Poore, Benjamin Perley. *History of Agriculture of the United States.* Report of the Commissioner of Agriculture. Washington. 1866

Roosevelt, Theodore. *Winning of the West.* New York. 1904

Sanford, Albert Hart. *The Story of Agriculture in the United States.* Boston. 1916

Schaefer, Joseph. *The Social History of American Agriculture.* New York. 1936

Schlesinger, Arthur M. and Dixon R. Fox, Eds. *History of American Life.* New York. 1927

Schmidt, Louis B. *Agriculture in the United States. Encyclopedia of the Social Sciences.* New York. 1930

Schmidt, Louis B. *Topical Studies and References on the Economic History of American Agriculture.* Philadelphia. 1919

Shaler, Nathaniel S. *Man and Nature in America.* New York. 1891

Shaler, N. S. *The United States of America.* 2 v. New York. 1894

Shannon, Fred Albert. *Economic History of the People of the United States.* New York. 1934.

Stine, O. C. *History of United States Agriculture.* In *Book of Rural Life.* Chicago. 1925

Treat, Payson Jackson. *The National Land System, 1785-1820.* New York. 1910

True, A. C. *Agricultural Education in the United States.* Department of Agriculture Yearbook. Washington. 1899

Turner, F. J. *The Frontier in American History.* New York. 1921

Tyron, Rolla M. *Household Manufactures in the United States, 1640-1860.* Chicago. 1917

United States Department of Agriculture. Many valuable publications including yearbooks and special bulletins. *Soils and Men,* 1938, is of outstanding excellence.

Upstream Engineering Conference. *Headwaters Control and Use.* United States Soil Conservation Service. Washington. 1936

Vandercook, J. W. *King Cane.* New York. 1939

Walker, Francis A. *American Agriculture*. United States Census Bureau.
Washington. 1880

Whitney, Milton. *Soil and Civilization*. New York. 1925

Everett E. Edwards, Associate Agricultural Economist, Division of Statistical and Historical Research, Bureau of Agricultural Economics, United States Department of Agriculture, has compiled a complete bibliography, published by the Department under the title *A Bibliography of the History of Agriculture in the United States*, Washington, November, 1930. Mr. Edwards has compiled a shorter book list, published by the Department in January, 1939, under the title *Selected References on the History of Agriculture in the United States*. Mr. Edwards also has written a brief factual account of *American Agriculture—The First 300 Years*, published (pages 171-277) in the 1940 Yearbook, Department of Agriculture. The Department's Yearbooks (1936-1942 inclusive) contain a mass of valuable agricultural material. Among the recent publications of the Department *What Is Farming?* (Washington, D. C., 1944) is a book prepared by the Department's specialists for the United States Armed Forces Institute. It is of great value to prospective farmers.

INDEX

343

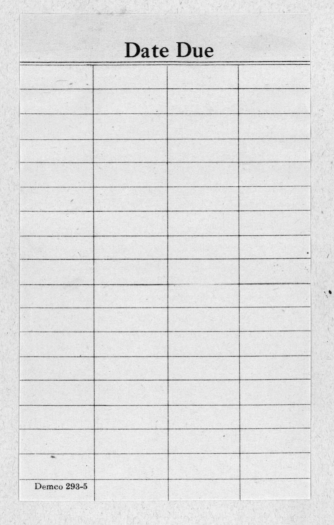

Date Due